ROMSEY
MILLS
&
WATERWAYS

A LTVAS Publication

by
Barbara Burbridge
Pat Genge
Jeff Hawksley
Mavis Hawksley
Nancy Kelly
Graham Langdon
Geoff Morris
(Editor: Barbara Burbridge)

© LTVAS 1998

ISBN No 0 9503980 6 3

Plate 1
A footbridge crosses the upper reaches of the Fishlake Stream
as it breaks away from the River Test on its journey to the centre of Romsey
Photograph taken in 1911

CONTENTS

Illustrations

INTRODUCTION

Romsey lies on the River Test, but a newcomer or visitor might well wonder how many River Tests there really are. Water is everywhere.

The water, however, is not as visible as in past centuries. In the town today streams appear, disappear and re-appear; it is all very confusing. West of the Market Place, through the Abbey gateway and some way into the one-time monastic precinct, one such stream emerges from underground. It flows behind a low stone wall along the south side of the road called The Abbey. Then it joins a broader waterway at the approach to the Town Memorial Park. Beyond the bridge at this point, and further along, a second bridge crosses yet another stream. Finally, the road narrows to a path that leads to a substantial footbridge-cum-sluice-gate, through which water rushes to a lower level. Here is Romsey's favourite beauty spot, the Salmon Leap, with the 18th-century Sadler's Mill as backdrop. Almost reduced now to the picturesque, these features offer positive clues to the historic importance of the river to the town.

This last waterway is, perhaps surprisingly, the River Test. 'Surprisingly' because it lies some way distant from the town with little but green fields between. The town itself is sensibly centred on higher land. Yet, although it skirts Romsey some distance away, the Test's importance is in no way diminished. This is the river that fills all but one strand of the confusing network of streams within the town itself. And it is that network, evolved over many centuries, that holds the key to Romsey's development.

Water was carried along the tracery of loops, braids and streams in and around firm, dry land, and attracted settlers from prehistoric times. Undoubtedly, those first inhabitants used the water and its natural resources with little direct intervention. Then, as time passed, primitive technology led to the manipulation of these waterways. The supports of simple bridges disturbed the flow. Natural water-meadows were supplemented by controlled irrigation of convenient grazing land. Streams were deepened or redirected to the advantage of various work processes, as well as more domestic uses. At the end of the 18th century a canal was cut to the east of the town as it then was; this canal, too, was fed by the River Test. Over the past twenty-five years or so archaeologists have found clear evidence of numerous ancient changes in the routes of Romsey's waterways, some perhaps natural but others deliberately made.

Mid-Saxon iron-smelters were probably the first intensive industrialists on the scene, using the nearby streams in the southern part of the settlement land. Then, from medieval times onwards, a more controlled network of waterways supplied the needs of Romsey's Benedictine nunnery, and was increasingly used in support of a whole range of local crafts and industries. Over the centuries it supplied tanneries, dye-works and breweries, all dependent on plentiful supplies of water. Generally, although its network of waterways was unique, Romsey's industry followed a pattern found in many similar-sized southern towns. Most unexpectedly, though, for an inland town such as Romsey, a boatyard was established by a long-serving 19th-century vicar of Romsey, the Rev. Edward Lyon Berthon. Water was essential for the work of his company.

Timelessly, the streams and rivers continued to flood the water-meadows in winter; they supplied the town with fish and eels; and they carried away the waste. Most dramatically of all, they powered the water-wheels of the mills that long underpinned the local economy. Initially, as elsewhere, there were only corn-mills but, over time, there were also fulling-mills, paper-mills, flax-mills, sawmills, mills for dressing leather and mills for grinding bones and chalk, as well as bark for the tanneries. For nearly a thousand years the water-mills lay at the heart of Romsey's prosperity.

The mills, powered by water from the river and the network of streams, played a crucial role in the history of the town. They were important to its economy, eventually providing employment for a considerable number of local people. As time passed and more mill sites were developed, the pressure on available water-power became ever more demanding. Documents relating to lengthy disputes, often involving subversive activities, reveal the vested interests that vied for the benefits accruing from the force of the river. They indicate that Romsey was more than just a market town. The surviving records of these disputes, particularly one of 1807, are the source of much information about Romsey's mills, and frequent reference will be made to them in the ensuing pages.

Regrettably, though some local use is still made of water from the River Test, the mills are now all closed; some have gone altogether, leaving no trace but memories. This book is an attempt to gather together some of those memories, to recall the days when Romsey was an important industrial centre, and to acknowledge the general debt of the town to its river.

THE RIVER TEST

The chairman of the National Rivers Authority, Lord Crickhowell, said that the River Test 'should be treated as a great work of art or music'. His statement implied the need to respect the delicate ecological balance of the river and to conserve its natural beauty, sustained throughout its length.

Such aesthetic appreciation of the river is, however, mainly a product of recent years. In the past the Test has been used primarily as a direct source of food, and of water for domestic and industrial uses, as well as a channel for the removal of every kind of waste from those activities. At Romsey, as elsewhere along its way, the river has been diverted to supply water-mills and the numerous water-meadows that used to surround the town. Corresponding cuts and drains have been made to return the used water further downstream. Despite this relentless onslaught, the river, with all its many braids, has survived as a very attractive feature in Hampshire.

Plate 2
The Fishlake approaching Romsey

The Test rises at Ashe, near Overton, to begin its 60-kilometre journey down to the sea via Southampton Water. Passing through Whitchurch, it picks up the Bourne rivulet and then meanders through a wide floodplain flanked by water-meadows, frequently splitting and joining again to form a network of braided channels. After being joined by the Dever, the Anton, Wallop Brook and the Dun it arrives on the outskirts of Romsey at Timsbury Bridge, just north of the *Duke's Head* public house on the Stockbridge road.

South of this point *(see plan of waterways inside back cover)* the water is split into three channels. The Fishlake strikes off towards Romsey town centre, and the main river passes under the bridge at Greatbridge with another major cut alongside supplying Greatbridge Mill. Further

7

downstream two more braids separate to supply first the old mill sites just to the north of Mill Lane and then the Rivermead complex. After this the main river is finally free to sweep around the western side of the relatively impermeable valley gravel on which the town is built. This gravel, which provides a firm building base, was deposited during the ice age that sculpted the valley over 10,000 years ago.

South-west of the town the Test passes Sadler's Mill, to be rejoined by the Fishlake immediately below Middlebridge. There it leaves Romsey town and enters Broadlands Park, where it is met by the Tadburn tributary. Within Broadlands Park the River Test flows rather closer than nature intended to the house, a testimony to the second Lord Palmerston. True to the spirit of the 18th century, he had the river redirected to improve his view.

The Chalk Stream Cycle

Most of the flow of the River Test is derived from rainwater, collected underground in the chalk subsoil. North of Mottisfont, indeed, the whole catchment area of the Test has a layer of chalk, which is very permeable to water. Chalk streams such as the Test produce very high quality water with a relatively even flow throughout the year. Curiously, only a proportion of the water appears in the Test: much more flows unseen through the river gravels.

In the winter, most of the rain soaks into the ground, taking several months to drain slowly down to the bottom of the valley. During summer, nearly all the rainfall is lost to evaporation and to transpiration by plants and trees. At this time, the river flow is dependent upon the stored underground water, which is at its maximum in spring and which declines slowly as autumn approaches. As a result of this extra underground supply for the summer months, the River Test has only a four to one variation in flow throughout the year, compared with several hundreds to one for rivers that derive their flow from less permeable catchment areas. Constancy of water supply has been very important in encouraging human settlement, and essential as a source of motive power for industrial purposes. The even flow also contributes directly to the natural beauty of the river. It allows the water to meander the length of the valley throughout the year with little 'freeboard' between the water surface and the top of the bank.

During its north-south journey around Romsey, from Greatbridge to Middlebridge, the river has a fall of some 6.7 metres. This fall provides Romsey with power equivalent to several hundred strong draught horses, working day and night, and needing no food. There is persuasive evidence of certain changes in water levels from medieval times onwards. More recently, the demands of the canal and drainage systems impacted on the main river. Nevertheless, the chalk stream river cycle seems always to have generated a significant potential power. Romsey millers at their peak took a good fraction of the total power available.

From Middlebridge, on the south-western edge of town, shadowy trout can be seen effortlessly holding their stations against the flow of the river, now moving briskly as it enters Broadlands Park. Here, though, the water does not betray the true extent of its remarkable power. This is more evident slightly upstream at Sadler's Mill, where the water gushes furiously through the by-pass sluice-gates.

Off-Shoots at Romsey: The Fishlake Stream & Related Waterways

Everybody needs water, and early people usually settled near streams or rivers. At Romsey the River Test offered high quality resources, but there was a danger of flooding in the immediate vicinity of the river banks. A long gravel platform to the east of the Test stood proud of the valley floor, and is now at the heart of historic Romsey. It must have tempted the earliest prehistoric people, but at that time its distance from the main river seems to have discouraged any settlement.

The Town's Natural Streams

From about 3,500 years ago, however, there was a direct supply of flowing water within the higher ground, even if it did not offer the range of resources found in and alongside the main river. The water came through an easterly braid of the Test. It may have emerged at Greatbridge where the Fishlake, its much-manipulated descendant, still begins its journey through the town.

This early natural stream, forced into existence by some eccentricity of landscape and weather, must have started with a force powerful enough to cut a deep way through the high gravel. It created a narrow valley through and beyond the area now bordered by the east end of Romsey Abbey and the west side of Church Street. Archaeologists have only been able to excavate pockets along the path of this water, making it difficult to plot the full line of its course, particularly the upper reaches. But they have established that in some places, such as behind the present Midland Bank in the Market Place, the water carved a channel to a depth some four to five metres below the present land surface. *(See Figure 2 on page 34 for street pattern.)*

9

To the south of the Market Place, the lower part of the stream was able to flow more easily down a shallow incline until reaching the low-lying area beyond Newton Lane. There a peat bog developed, through which numerous streamlets deposited slender fingers of gravel. On the south-western edge of the bog a more substantial ancient waterway eventually dried out. It left a deep layer of white river gravel on which Middlebridge Street still wends its way through otherwise peaty wetland.

Over time the line of the 'town' stream changed, perhaps several times and for a variety of reasons. The earliest artefacts associated with the bed of this stream date back to the Late Middle Bronze age, c1200BC. By 700-800BC Bronze age people were obstructing water flow with foundation stakes for walkway bridges, and inserting stretches of substantial piling against the banks of the Test south of Romsey. As people increasingly intervened, the flow of water varied in strength, now flowing deep and hard, then slowing and silting up, gradually changing the depth and force of the waterway.

Controlling the Fishlake
In the area north of Newton Lane, mid-Saxon iron-smelters undoubtedly had an impact on the stream. Slag from their work processes has been found in the old stream beds, but there is little evidence that they sought to make positive improvements. Then, later, as the medieval settlement evolved around the nunnery precinct, the need arose for a more controlled flow of water into the heart of the town. Two major ambitions inspired the work that took place. One was the desire to organise a water supply to the Abbey precinct, established by the early 10th century. The other was the idea of developing an urban mill at the southern end of the gravel 'island', where a comparatively sharpish landfall could maximise the power of the water. The authority vested in the high-status nunnery, endorsed by royal charters, undoubtedly provided the impetus for such an enterprise.

Using early medieval technology, men set to work on the existing flow of water through the town. It appears that the aim was to divert and channel the 'Church Street' watercourse to form a boundary for the east and south sides of the monastic precinct. By manipulating the natural stream now known as the Fishlake, it would have been comparatively easy to construct such a route around the Abbey.

The upper reaches of the Fishlake still follow an erratic course, endorsing the idea that this initial stretch had its origin in a natural outlet from the Test.

Downstream, as it approached the northern edge of the town, the medieval watercourse needed some assistance. This was partly because it was on a shallower gradient than the main river, partly, perhaps, because of silting, once the initial surge of water had slowed to a much more moderate pace. The solution was to constrain the flow of the Fishlake within an 'embanked' channel, clearly visible today from the Stockbridge Road. Changes in the surrounding land may have exaggerated the height of the embankment over time, but the straightness of the banks at this point was certainly the result of deliberate canalisation. This work would have improved the flow of a stream that had become too sluggish for the new demands to be placed upon it.

The archaeological evidence, as already cited, supports the view that the Fishlake naturally continued a slightly south-westerly course towards the Abbey. There it was coerced along the eastern boundary of the Abbey precinct. It then continued on a southerly line towards Newton Lane; for centuries the most useful purpose of this lower section of the stream was reflected in its name, the Shitlake. (The numerous privies built over it, recorded in documents and later depicted on large-scale 19th-century Ordnance Survey maps, confirm the use to which this stream was put by successive generations. Although its course varied slightly over time, the Shitlake was a substantial watercourse, only more recently reduced to a drain. Before its final disappearance underground, documents recorded the more genteel, alternative title of Bell Street Lake.)

Just south of the gateway into the monastic precinct some of the water destined for the Shitlake was diverted westward into Abbey Water. This deliberately-made cut would have reduced the flooding south of Newton Lane, but its main purpose was undoubtedly to serve the Abbey and delineate the southern boundary of the main precinct. It is probably pre-13th century in date. Abbey Water was known as the 'still waters' at the time of the dissolution of Romsey Abbey in 1539. By 1551 at least, it had become the pond supplying a water-mill located at the junction of Abbey Water with Narrow Lane. Though still a fairly broad stream, old photographs show that the Abbey Water mill-pond was narrowed during the 20th century.

At various times the Fishlake has been called the 'Fishlet', and this may help to explain its purpose. 'Let(t)' is an old spelling for 'leat', meaning an open watercourse to conduct water for household or industrial purposes. So the Fishlake/Fishlet name may come from the ultimate destination of the westerly branch that curved round the Abbey precinct, namely the monastic fishponds. Archaeologists have established that these were on the site of the present vicarage, beyond the west end of the Abbey church. During the time of the nunnery an off-shoot from Abbey Water flowed northwards, just outside the western precinct wall (and through the present Abbey Meads Surgery land), to supply fresh water to these fishponds.

A minor watercourse, controlled by a hatch, and once leading westwards off the Fishlake by No 6 Church Street, can only be traced back to the 18th century. It may be much older, though, perhaps starting as a water supply to the domestic range of the Abbey precinct. Only someone of considerable authority could have diverted the main flow of the Fishlake in such a way. It would certainly have been most unpopular with the post-dissolution millers at Abbey Mill. There is no evidence to date about the existence or possible use of this watercourse within the medieval Abbey precinct.

The Holbrook
At the northern end of the old *Horsefair Brewery* site, an easterly branch of the Fishlake flows southwards under the name of Holbrook, or archaically 'Holebrok'. Confusingly, the Holbrook name was once used more extensively for the full length of the stream from Greatbridge. Indeed, the oldest reference yet found for the Holbrook links it with property unquestionably near the stream's upper reaches. Long before any known use of the 'Fishlake' name, this document confirms the existence of the Holbrook as a waterway in the early 13th century. However, it makes no reference to the Holbrook leading to and powering the Town Mill (at the lower end of present-day Bell Street). The first discovered date for that function is 1363.

The Holbrook south of the old *Horsefair Brewery* is very straight. Whether it was preceded by a natural stream is more problematical than in the case of its westerly neighbour. Certainly, archaeological examination has revealed that the banks were artificially built up, but there has been no opportunity to establish if natural banks lie behind, or near, this work. (There is always the possibility that early technicians created the Holbrook at the expense of another waterway that may have flowed along Latimer Street to the east. The old spelling for this name, 'Lortemere', possibly meant slow-moving water. However, any suggestion that the lower Holbrook is a post-Saxon, man-made cut has serious implications for the manorial boundary between Romsey Infra and Romsey Extra. The Fishlake/Holbrook long acted as the boundary between these two manors, and any suggestion of a change in the line of the lower Holbrook would equally suggest a change to that boundary.)

Whatever its origins, the eventual medieval purpose of the easterly channel, the lower Holbrook, was to power the Town Mill. Those working and living alongside its length, however, would have placed supplementary demands upon its water. These demands, though, were dependent on the permission of the stream owners, initially the Abbess of Romsey Abbey, and subsequently the secular owners of the Town Mill. Nothing was to interrupt the power to the mill. (It should be remembered that many property owners had access to wells for supplies of fresh water.)

The tail race from the Town Mill passed under a bridge at the entrance to Banning Street (now the start of Broadwater Road), and then proceeded along the south-east side of Middlebridge Street. At this point, the ancient boundary between Romsey Infra and Romsey Extra, having followed the Fishlake/Holbrook from Greatbridge, deviated south from the street line and followed Chavy Water. This was once a substantial waterway linking through to Tadburn Lake, an independent tributary of the River Test. The historic importance of Chavy Water suggests that the lower reaches of the Holbrook in Middlebridge Street were only given prominence, or even first cut, in the post-medieval period. This lower stretch may have been enhanced for the benefit of the tanning industry, long established in that area.

The Fishlake/Holbrook combination served the town well, its usefulness outliving the days of the Benedictine nuns. More recently, in the 19th century, the name Holbrook for the easterly branch was temporarily superseded by 'Back Stream' or 'Shutlands Stream' in certain documents, adding to the earlier confusion between Fishlake, Fishlet and Holbrook. Whatever its name, the development of the two-pronged stream was a tribute to medieval ingenuity, and undoubtedly a most important factor in the development of the town.

The Modern Fishlake

To achieve a smooth flow through the town, water from the River Test enters the Fishlake Stream almost two kilometres upstream to the north of the town. Immediately after entering the Greatbridge Industrial Estate, on the edge of town, the Fishlake flows along Romsey's only aqueduct, a construction of unknown date and much altered over the years. Beneath this aqueduct an east-west stream drains Fishlake Meadows, and carries any overflow from the 'Barge' canal to the east and the Fishlake itself. The western section of this 'under' stream has a long history as Horsehead Ditch, mentioned in medieval documents.

The Fishlake Stream is not a minor waterway, but is quite wide, capable of carrying about a third of the water accumulated in the River Test at the point of separation. These days a sluice, just below the road called Fishlake Meadows and close to the aqueduct, diverts most of the water through Horsehead Ditch to Test Mill Stream, and thus back into the main river. As a result of this diversion only a comparatively tiny amount of water now makes its way through the town, where it is no longer needed industrially. The Fishlake's large potential capacity would, undoubtedly, have encouraged the medieval concept of using it for working water-wheels and meeting the requirements of the Abbey community, both major purposes.

The smaller amount of water that is now allowed to continue down the lower reaches of the Fishlake moves much more slowly than upstream of the sluice-gate. It can no longer wash along as much silt as before. The deposition of silt, and the resulting slowness of the water, has affected the ecology. Vegetation and animal life has changed to meet new conditions. The Environmental Agency has created a 'funnel' near the Fishlake aqueduct to help restore the balance. The funnel is some tens of metres long, narrowing downstream, and the water is channelled down its mouth at a higher speed. The sides of the funnel are made by driving wooden stakes into the bed of the Fishlake and connecting them with wire and hessian to form two fences. The hessian rapidly fills up with silt and weeds to form a fairly impermeable wall. Fences such as these, sometimes called 'hedges', have been used for centuries, although their earlier purpose was to deflect eels and fish into traps or to encourage water to flow from one stream into another.

South of the fork at the old *Horsefair Brewery* site it is difficult nowadays to follow the course of either branch of the Fishlake Stream. Each frequently disappears underground during its passage through the town centre. This is the result of work initiated by the 19th-century Pavement Commission, which sacrificed open water to the cause of pavements and ease of movement around the town. The eastern branch of the stream (the Holbrook) may be seen behind the garden of the 13th-century King John's House, and again to the west of the bus station. Between these two points, however, it has passed quite unobtrusively through a culvert running under the junction of the Market Place with The Hundred, where evidence of a once important bridge has been erased. South of the bus station, it is easy to follow the stream's passage through the Duke's Mill Shopping Precinct. Its tumbling fall at this point marks the centuries-long existence of the Town Mill. Unfortunately, this time-honoured name has been overlooked. The shopping precinct now on the site has taken instead the name of the last owner, James Duke, who bought the mill around 1935.

Leaving the site of the Town Mill, the Holbrook passes under the Bell Street end of Broadwater Road to continue in the open again along the south side of Middlebridge Street, and thence to the main river under the eastern end of Middlebridge itself. Intriguingly, there is a half-hidden small stream, little more than a ditch, turning off alongside No 24 Middlebridge Street. This is all that remains of the medieval Chavy Water.

Much of the other leg of the Fishlake Stream is also hidden underground. After making a brief appearance at the north-eastern edge of Church Street it now crosses this street unseen, and continues hidden along the western side of the street and of the Market Place. It only re-appears just beyond the Abbey gateway, where it curves round the United Reformed Church into the one-time 'still waters' of the Abbey. There are two outlets downstream from the old Abbey Mill site. The most visible may be followed along the south side of the road called The Abbey until it joins Test Mill Stream. This is Coleman's Ditch, named after Dr Coleman who, in the early 1800s, lived in the large house just to the west of the gateway that leads into the modern Convent of La Sagesse. Water from the second outlet still flows under and across the grounds of La Sagesse Convent. It, too, feeds into Test Mill Stream but further south, just before it joins the main river. Another ancient stream once flowed through the playing fields of the old convent school, but its line is now only visible on aerial photographs.

Even after much of the water had been hidden underground, the town's inner streams remained of practical importance to the community. Indeed, an event in 1876 illustrates the continuing dependence of the town on its central waterway. In that year the closure of the Fishlake, for the repair of a break in the banks, left the mills without power and the town without refuse disposal.

The Fishlake/Holbrook has been the unfortunate recipient of assorted pollutants, from woad by-products out of medieval dye-shops to more recent brewing effluent. It was long abused and neglected by those who should have scoured its depths and maintained its banks. But it played a vital role in Romsey's history. Although nowadays only of an aesthetic value that should not be under-estimated, the town's inner waterways continued to be of industrial and domestic significance to the town through to the 20th century.

Off-Shoots of the River Test at Romsey: An Old Meander & Convenient Cuts

A great complex braid breaks eastwards from the River Test and passes through the Mill Lane area before rejoining the main river at the southernmost tip of the Town Memorial Park. It may possibly be the echo of an ancient meander that once brought the main flow of water closer to the raised platform of gravel in the prehistoric era. Undoubtedly, it offered a sufficiently strong flow of water to power the water-wheels that were set up in early medieval times just off to the north of Mill Lane. The sites around Test Mill and Mead Mill were probably the easiest ones for medieval technicians to develop for milling purposes, the water at these locations providing the most natural potential.

In the 18th century a short but effective cut helped to develop water-wheels at Burnt Mill, just to the south of Mead Mill, whilst a long narrow one made possible expansion on the Rivermead site further south. The latter cut, for reasons that are obvious on large-scale maps of the area, was known as the Straight Stream.

Tadburn Lake

Tadburn Lake ('lake' being formerly used for a stream) rises in Ampfield Woods, some four miles east of Romsey. It runs along the southern edge of the town alongside the by-pass, where it is joined by Chavy Water. It is the odd-one-out of Romsey's streams, being a tributary rather than an off-shoot of the River Test, and flowing east to west. At times it has been called Spittle Tadburn or Tadburn Spittle. This acknowledged the fact that on its way, near Botley Road, it passed the southern boundary of the medieval hospital or 'spittle' of St Mary and St Anthony, Romsey's leper hospital.

The Tadburn is not a true chalk stream like the Test, so its flow is more immediately responsive to rainfall. In exceptional conditions it flooded before it could join the Test below Middlebridge. Flooding has not been confined to the Tadburn. During the last 150 years fourteen serious floods have been recorded, the water-meadows adjacent to Greatbridge Road being the most frequent location. Nevertheless, the Tadburn flood of October 1960 was one of the most dramatic; townspeople had the opportunity to travel down Palmerston Street by boat. (Essential improvements were then made.) In other moods, the Tadburn was never a prolific or dependable source of power. It needed an additional supply of water from the Andover-Redbridge Canal before it was successfully used to drive a mill, namely Fox Mill.

In the past the joint waters of the Tadburn and Chavy Water split after a short distance. One section continued westwards towards Middlebridge, whilst the other flowed southwards across the line now followed by the Romsey by-pass and so into Broadlands Park. The latter stream is now in a culvert, flowing under both the by-pass and the lawn within the park. The westward line has been cut off, leaving only a usually dry ditch to indicate its past existence.

Water-meadows

Apart from the major waterways around and through the town, there is a myriad of minor waterways along the Test Valley. Some of these were simply dug as ditches to drain the land, but the majority were part of complex schemes to irrigate meadows, known as water-meadows.

The term water-meadows has always been used casually to describe river-side meadows that flood naturally from time to time, such as those between Romsey and Timsbury. The grass in these flooded meadows grew quickly, providing an 'early bite' for grazing at a time when fodder stored over winter was running out and the next year's growth on dry meadows was not yet ready. The advantage of this provision was well appreciated, and the Tapsham meadows alongside Mead Mill Stream may represent early attempts at creating deliberate water-meadows.

Large-scale development of controlled water-meadows took place throughout Wessex from about 1650 to 1750, and had a huge impact on the landscape of the river valleys. By the late 1700s almost all suitable land near the rivers had been developed for this purpose. Attempts to create water-meadows in other parts of the country were generally unsuccessful or uneconomic, because the techniques employed owed their success to the special characteristics of chalk streams. The town of Romsey was practically surrounded by water-meadows, and they extended up the River Test most of the way to Andover. They have now fallen into disuse, but their imprints can be found scattered all along the valley in the form of meadows with ridges about one or two feet high, together with a maze of ditches and rivulets.

The creation of water-meadows required considerable skill and experience. The desired results were achieved by intermittently flooding the meadows with water diverted from the river during winter and early spring. Men who operated and maintained the meadows were known as 'mead men' or 'drowners'. Rivers such as the Test, which derive their water from underground, where it has been stored for several months, maintain a fairly even temperature throughout the year. The relatively warm water carries a considerable amount of chalk. This is generally thought to be a significant factor in encouraging the growth of grass by reducing the acidity of the soil, particularly in peaty areas. It also contains mineral-rich sediment, deposited during flooding and acting as a top-dressing of fertiliser. Additionally, the water becomes heavily oxygenated during its journey down the generally wide and shallow river course. All these factors played a part in encouraging an early growth of luxuriant grass in the water-meadows. They help to explain why these meadows were so much more successful in Wessex (which contains many chalk streams) than in other parts of the country.

Flooding was usually stopped around the beginning of March, and the meadows were allowed to dry out so that grazing could begin in April. The first grass crop obtained in this way was generally some 4-6 weeks ahead of that produced by ordinary meadows, and was of great value to farmers at this time of the year. After the grazing period, the channels in the meadows were usually repaired near the middle of May, and flooded again to encourage a hay crop in July. For this crop it was advised that the grass should be cut 'young and in full sap', as water-meadow grass was said to be coarse if left to grow too long. Sometimes a second crop of hay, the aftermath, could be obtained by repeating the whole process.

Types of Water-Meadows
During the hey-day of man-made water-meadows there were two main types. These were known as 'catch-work meadows' and 'flowing (or floated) meadows'. Catch-work meadows were relatively simple in construction. They were formed by diverting part of a river along a hillside via a hatch, stopping the end and allowing the water to overflow in a sheet down the hillside back into the river below. This type of water-meadow was best suited to country where there was considerable slope on the land. The more complicated 'flowing meadow' construction was preferable around Romsey, and along the Test Valley generally, because the gentle slope of the valley down to the sea made drainage of the land very difficult after simple 'catch-work' flooding.

'Flowing' meadows were constructed by building a weir at a suitable point on the river in order to raise the water level, and by digging out a new 'cut' just above the weir to carry the water down to the meadows to be irrigated. A hatch to control the supply of water to the meadows was built close to the weir. This varied in style from a simple board running across the new cut to more complicated, mechanically-operated gates. The cut was known as the main carrier and on arrival at the water-meadow it was diverted into a number of furrows dug into the tops of ridges. Typically these ridges were about three feet high and twenty feet apart (see Figure 1). They were filled to the brim, and the water was intended to flow at grass root level (rather than cover the whole plant) down the sides of the ridges into the drains or 'drawns'. These were connected so that the water returned to the river.

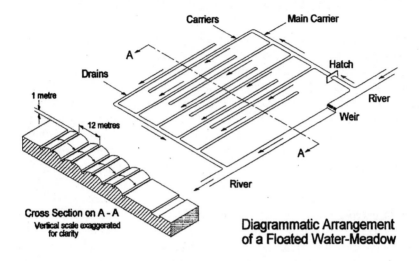

Figure 1: Diagram of a Water-Meadow

Main carriers could be cut with a slightly lesser fall than the main river. By the time they reached the water-meadow, they had gained sufficient height to allow the water to drain back into the river. To achieve this height above river level, the carriers were often a mile or more in length and if they fed a number of water-meadows could be comparable in size to the main river.

Water-meadows were used extensively along the River Test during the 17th and 18th centuries, but they never really recovered from the depression that followed the Napoleonic wars. They went into a slow decline as farming methods changed, labour costs rose, and new crops were introduced and used as winter feed. The legacy they left made a large contribution to the complex of waterways and ridged meadows to be found around Romsey town. A few working water-meadows are still to be found in the Wessex region.

1942: Dispute over Development of the Test Valley

Disputes between different groups of users of the River Test, notably millers, fishermen and farmers, have occurred through the ages. The most persistent were those between the various mills, as rival millers vied for sufficient water power. These arguments will be considered later. It is appropriate here, however, to describe a more recent, and unusual, contretemps that took place during the Second World War. It had an impact on the river valley from Kimbridge, to the north of Romsey, down as far as the sea.

From the onset of the war, the Ministry of Agriculture, recognising that the country's food supply was at risk, was looking for waste land that could be turned to productive use. By that time, the old water-meadow system, which had been so extensive in the 1700s, had long since been abandoned. Hatches had broken, and waterways intended as occasional conduits had become fishing streams. Without the incentive of the water-meadows to keep the river dredged, it had silted up, and the water level had risen substantially. This in turn had caused the old water-meadows, and much of the other surrounding land, to become permanently waterlogged and unproductive.

In 1942, the Ministry of Agriculture set up a Catchment Board for Hampshire's rivers, with the recovery of marshy and waterlogged land as one of its objectives. This was the signal for battle to commence between landowners, fishermen and farmers. The fishermen and landowners, who made a good living from river sport, claimed that the Ministry would ruin them, together with the finest salmon and trout river in the country. The farmers, who had everything to gain, since dredging the river would be funded by the Ministry, claimed that thousands of acres of productive land could be brought back into use. Eventually, the argument was resolved by a compromise, by which the Ministry would dredge the river from Kimbridge down to the sea, and the fisheries were allowed the river above Kimbridge.

The Catchment Board then commenced dredging, creating a substantial drop in the level of the river and a small waterfall just below the bridge at Kimbridge, which was the limit of the Board's territory. Where it had been dredged, the land on either side of the river dried out and work began on recovering it.

At Fishlake Meadows in Romsey, some areas were brought back into full arable rotation. In other places, notably alongside Horsebridge Station further up the Test Valley, water-meadows were restored; but, generally, the majority of the land was reseeded and used as dry meadows for grazing. The success of this project, as measured at the time, was only partial. Much of the land so recovered fell back into disuse, because the farmers did not have sufficient capital and resources to develop or sustain their new land. By present day reckoning, however, their failure to do so might well be recorded as an environmental success, since these areas in their natural form provide a habitat for many threatened species.

The Canal and Other Waterways

Owing no debt to nature, other than the source of its water supply, the canal was a late-comer to Romsey's system of waterways, and very much more to the east than any of them. The pleasant waterside walk towards the Stockbridge Road, accessed to the west of the Plaza Theatre, follows the one-time towpath for the Romsey section of the Andover-Redbridge Canal. The idea for such a canal was aired in the 17th century, but did not reach fulfilment until the end of the 18th century. The route was surveyed in 1770 by Robert Whitworth (whose name is remembered in Romsey's *Robert Whitworth Drive* off Fishlake Meadows). He was both surveyor and foreman to a famous name in canal history, James Brindley. Despite having 24 locks, Whitworth's canal was only 22 miles long. Consequently, there was no need for living accommodation on the barges, and a number of bargees lived in Romsey. Completed in the mid-1790s, the canal was in use until 1859, when it was bought by the Andover to Southampton Railway. Much of the canal bed was used as the base for the new railway, but the Romsey stretch, popularly known as the Barge, was saved by Lord Palmerston's efforts. He negotiated for the railway to run even further than intended away from his Broadlands estate.

During the canal's hey-day Romsey was served by a wharf, situated, it is thought, on the south-west of the Plaza roundabout. Traffic was mostly in materials concerned with the agricultural community, or the building and tanning trades. Shortly before closure the goods transported were listed at 2,033 tons, comprising corn, coals, building materials, artificial manure, soda, hides and bark. In the beginning, it had been hoped that the canal would link up with the Basingstoke Canal to provide a through route to London, via the Rivers Wey and Thames, but this did not materialise, leaving the canal with local trade only. Failure to complete the Southampton-Salisbury Canal, the 'Bankrupt Canal', which would have looped through Romsey, also left the Andover-Redbridge Canal isolated.

Bridging the Waterways

Whilst the waterways were the life-blood of early Romsey, they were also a hindrance to movement within and beyond the town's developing street pattern. Bridges were, therefore, an important feature of the area. On the main river the town was approached via Timsbury Bridge and Greatbridge to the north and Middlebridge to the south-west. At one time there was another bridge further south within Broadlands. This was Waldron's Bridge, pulled down by the second Lord Palmerston in the late 18th century.

Crossing the many braids within the town itself there were carriage bridges, footbridges and private bridges. Heavy traffic was controlled, whether intentionally or not, by the need to follow the larger bridges that could provide the necessary width, and accept the load. Residual evidence suggests that there were also fords at certain locations, but these gain no mention in documents. It is the subject of bridges that haunts the records with stories of endless struggles to assign responsibility for their upkeep and repairs.

It was the 19th-century Pavement Commissioners who began the gradual replacement of bridges with culverts under level roadways. Nowadays drivers and pedestrians alike are scarcely aware of crossing numerous waterways on a journey around town.

Plate 3

The River Test leaving Romsey at Middlebridge and entering Broadlands Park. This is a view of the 18th-century bridge, taken c1890 before it was rebuilt at a lower level during construction of the Romsey by-pass in the 1930s

Editorial Note: A full study of Romsey's bridges is expected to be included in a forthcoming publication.

22

NATURE FIRST: The Natural Resources of the River

The River Test has been a constant source of water and food for those who have settled near, or visited, its banks. Over the centuries it has supplied the necessities of life to countless generations, and continues to do so. Today, though, the direct link with the natural resource has been lost. Customers buying their farmed fish at the supermarket seldom pause to think that it may have come from a local fish farm on the River Test. At home, people are even less likely to appreciate that their domestic water supply is 'on tap' because the water board takes huge amounts from the river. Prehistoric people, and their successors through to the early 20th century, were much more aware of their dependence on the waterways. The miller, living in close proximity to the various watercourses, was a particularly shrewd user of many of the resources available in and around the river. Latterly, though, the balance has shifted more in favour of recreation.

Eels

One of the profitable sidelines for the miller was the harvesting of eels. Earlier generations were always on the look-out for sources of protein, and considered the humble eel a great delicacy. They were then, as they are now, preserved by smoking. The Abbey valued them so highly that, in the 15th century, the Abbess decreed that part of the rental of the Town Mill and Mead Mill should be paid in eels. Centuries later, when the railway first arrived in Romsey (1847), eels were transported live to London where a better price could be obtained. In the 1950s jellied-eel manufacturers collected their live raw material from this area, employing lorries equipped with oxygenated water tanks. Indeed, there is still an unobtrusive but lucrative trade in the supply of local eels to the smoked- and jellied-eel market. Generally, though, little heed is now paid to these 'water snakes', except by the few directly involved in the modern eel trade, and anglers dislike them for leaving their fishing lines tangled and covered with slime.

The freshwater eel has an extraordinary life cycle. The baby eel hatches from an egg in the Sargasso Sea, just east of Mexico. It then makes its way across the Atlantic Ocean and up the European rivers where it eats voraciously and grows up to a metre in length. Around seven years of age the eel has the urge to return to its spawning ground, and, in the autumn when conditions are right, it sets off downstream. It is so determined to reach its ultimate destination, the Sargasso Sea, that, if necessary, it will slither across damp fields, breathing through its skin. At this stage, the eels

23

have reached their maximum weight and have changed colour from a yellow hue to silver. These 'silver eels', as they are termed, are a prized catch.

Plate 4
Eel-trap at Test Mill, 1996

If the eel is to be captured, there is nowhere better to catch it than in a section of the river where the channel is narrow, and the water can be diverted through a suitable trap. That is where the miller, with his ready-made channels, took advantage. He collected the eels by lowering an iron grill with narrow gaps into the mill stream. Sometimes he diverted the water through a special channel on to the grill. However, the miller had to be canny. If he left the grill in the stream all the time, it would be blocked by detritus in the form of weeds and worse. The skilled miller would study the portents for good eel migrations, the phase of the moon, the river level, the expectation of rain, etc., before setting the trap. If there was a good run of eels, he might stay up all night removing the eels and clearing weed from the traps. On a good night, hundreds of eels could be caught.

Most Romsey mills seem to have had eel-traps. The Town Mill arrangement had an extra sophistication. A glazed-earthenware pipe of four-inch (10cm) diameter was installed, running from the eel-trap grill to a collecting basket immersed in the stream. The eels were kept alive in the basket ready for transportation. At Greatbridge Mill eel-traps were installed in the space previously occupied by the water-wheel after the wheel had been removed.

24

Millers had to obtain permission to catch eels from the owner of the river at the point where the mill was located. In a late 19th-century conveyance for Mead Mill the rights were carefully detailed. 'And also the right of Eel Fishery at Mead Mills and of laying ports or other engines for catching fish at the waste water hatches there.'

Trout and Salmon

Plate 5
A salmon leaping at the Salmon Leap
by Sadler's Mill

The management of salmon and trout is in no way a modern phenomenon.

Owners of river banks have long jealously guarded their fishing rights, reserving them when leasing riverside property. In 1428, when the Abbess of Romsey Abbey leased a site for a new fulling-mill on Chavy Water to William Berrell, she stipulated that he was not to take fish without her permission. It is difficult to discover, though, whether there were very early wide-spread laws relating specifically to maintenance of good fish supplies in rivers.

By the early 18th century, however, legal provision had certainly been made to ensure free passage of fish up and down rivers, and there were restrictions as to when fish could be caught. Justices of the Peace and millers were required to discharge their responsibilities for fish management, as laid down by Parliament. Overleaf is a local warning notice issued in the 19th century by the County of Southampton, an old name for Hampshire. It usefully summarises the provisions of legislation enacted in the reigns of Queen Anne and George III. It is interesting to note the local names for fish at their various stages of development in the following extracts. It is also interesting to note the severity of the scale of fines and penalties for that time, aimed at poachers as well as those failing to provide for the welfare of game-fish. Salmon and trout management was obviously a serious business.

EXTRACTS FROM THE
ACTS OF PARLIAMENT
FOR THE
PRESERVATION OF SALMON, &c.

WITHIN THE COUNTIES OF SOUTHAMPTON AND WILTS.

By the 4 of Anne, *It is enacted.*--That all owners and Occupiers of Corn, Fulling, Paper and other Mills, upon any of the Waters in the said Counties, shall keep open for a certain period therein mentioned, one Scuttle or a small Hatch of a foot square in the waste Hatch or Watercourse, in the direct Stream where no water-wheel standeth, for the Salmon to pass and re-pass freely up and down the River and that no Person (not being duly qualified by Law,) shall kill, destroy, or wilfully hurt any Salmon and Salmon kind, or any other Fish under the Pains, Penalty, Forfeitures and Imprisonments, therein mentioned. For the first Trespass or Offence, not less than 20s. or more than £5; for the second Trespass or Offence, not less than 40s. or more than £10; and as the Trespass or Offence increase, to double the Penalty; and in default of Payment, to be sent to the House of Correction.

By the 37 Geo.3, *It is enacted.*--That it shall be lawful for the Owners and Proprietors and every other Person entitled to fish in the Rivers within the said Counties, between the 1st Day of January and the 12th Day of September, to take, kill, and destroy, any Salmon, Salmon Peal or Salmon kind or Bouges, (commonly called Sea Trouts,) and offer the same for sale. But no such Owner, Proprietor or other Person aforesaid, shall at any Time or Times between the 12th Day of September and the 1st Day of January, take, kill, or wilfully hurt, any Salmon, Salmon Peal or Salmon kind or Bouges, or offer for Sale any of the Fish so taken; under the like Pains, Penalties and Forfeitures, as are mentioned in the above recited Act.

And that the Justices of the Peace for the said Counties, respectively residing within 5 Miles of any of the said Rivers, shall, and are hereby directed and required once in any year at any Quarter or Special Sessions, on or before the 1st Day of November, to assign Overseers for the Purpose of the said recited Act.

And it is also enacted, (it being considered expedient to extend the time limited by the said recited Act.) That all Owners and Occupiers of Mills upon the said Rivers, shall constantly keep open the said small Scuttle or Hatch, in manner directed by the said recited Act, from the 11th Day of November to the 11th Day of July in every Year under the like Pains, Penalties and Forfeitures, as are contained in the said recited Act.

26

One of the facilities built under the above act afforded a popular autumnal spectacle in Romsey for many years. People gathered at Sadler's Mill to watch the salmon using the salmon leap to by-pass the powerful sluices. Until recently, the arches over the main sluice gate were padded with sacks of straw to prevent the salmon from injuring themselves when jumping. Within the last few years, however, the river authority has installed a more effective, but less dramatic, salmon pass on the east side of the sluices.

Wild Fowl

Duck shooting along the river banks was not universally common and was confined to marshy areas such as Oxlease, just north of Romsey. The general practice was for the local gentry to have ponds on their property to which the ducks were attracted by regular feeding. Every three weeks or so there was a morning or evening shoot when ducks were culled as they flew in to land. A variation on this theme was to frighten the ducks off a pond, such as the one at Ridge, and then shoot them from prepared hides as they flew along the river. Decoy ponds with trapping nets, common elsewhere, seem not to have been employed in the Romsey area.

Snipe shooting was common in the early 20th century, when the flood meadows were actively maintained or left as wet areas. The meadows at flooding time acted as a magnet for the local snipe, but these birds disappeared when the meadows dried up and the marshes were drained.

Moorhens were a popular source of food up to the 1930s. It was common practice to collect and eat moorhens' eggs, and moorhen stew was also enjoyed. Numbers have decreased in recent years mainly due to the presence of mink, an alien species now naturalised.

Recreational Angling

Fishing, as a recreation, was famously publicised in the book 'The Compleat Angler', written by a retired Winchester linen draper, Izaak Walton, in 1653. The fifth edition, published in 1676, even contained a supplement on fly fishing written by his poet friend, Charles Cotton.

The sport won the approval of the aristocracy in the early 19th century, when it became fashionable for country gentlemen to invite guests to their estates to fish for trout. The attraction lay in identifying a particular fish lying at its station in the river, and then enticing it to take the fly.

During the mid-19th century, the treeless banks of the River Test on either side of Romsey would have appeared desolate compared with today. Fly-fishing was than undertaken with a bamboo pole and silk line, and the angler relied upon the wind to carry the fly over the water. Trees were considered a menace to effective casting and were cut down. The introduction of the modern split cane 'whipping' rod in the 1880s, and the tapered line, allowed casting to become independent of the wind, and the trees were allowed to grow once more. This was an unusual instance of modern technology aiding the environment. Technology also helped the fishermen. The development of the artificial fly extended the season well past the narrow limits dictated by the life-span of the mayfly.

Originally, salmon were perceived by trout anglers as a pest because they destroyed the spawning grounds of the trout. Fishing expeditions were organised to catch the young salmon, which were then consumed at 'smolt suppers'. In the 1920s serious consideration was given to placing a barrier at Sadler's Mill to prevent salmon from penetrating further up the river. Eventually, though, the salmon's larger size and greater fighting ability attracted anglers. The river below Romsey became famous for its salmon fishing, whilst the river upstream was prized for its trout. Little love existed between the two angling fraternities.

The latter half of the 19th century also ushered in a more organised approach to game-fishing with the advent of the fishing club. Groups of like-minded, upper class members of the fishing fancy leased stretches of game-fish rivers from the land owners. As angling became more popular, the natural fish stocks became depleted, and the clubs took on the responsibility of managing fish stocks and replenishing the river as necessary. Fish-breeding took place in 'stew ponds' where the fish were hatched from spawn and reared before being introduced into the river. The destructive effect of the salmon was no longer a serious problem, and the animosity between trout and salmon anglers faded.

The stew ponds at Broadlands were constructed from the high and low sluice streams that were made redundant when the practice of flooding the water-meadows was discontinued. The high sluice aqueduct was slate-lined.

The Houghton Club, based at Stockbridge, is one of the most famous angling clubs in the world. Unusually, the club owns stretches of the Test and the adjacent land. It is very select, membership being by invitation only.

Recently, the membership has been allowed to increase from 18 to 24. Today, game-fishing is 'big business'. In addition to established fishing clubs, control has passed to syndicates that lease the rights from landowners, and rent out 'beats' to clubs or individual anglers.

Considerable effort is required to maintain the River Test either side of Romsey as a game-fish river. Coarse fish are a problem, the pike eating the game-fish and the grayling eating the food. They were once removed by netting after the weeds had been cut. Some local landowners upstream of Romsey also used to organise fishing events for grayling, at which members of local coarse fishing clubs were invited. This provided good sport and helped to promote good public relations across the general spectrum of the fishing fraternity. These practices have, in the main, been replaced by electric stunning of the fish, which are then removed and placed in dedicated coarse fish lakes such as Broadlands lakes just south of the M27 at Nursling. Electric stunning is more effective where the river is narrow. Below Romsey, where the various streams merge, it is less so. Lord Mountbatten used to invite fishing clubs with naval connections to take out the coarse fish. Recently, the Broadlands sections of the river have been leased for coarse fishing with the proviso that all catches be returned.

The health of the fish must be monitored closely. In 1967 the disease 'Ulcerative Dermal Necrosis' (UDN) found its way into the river and attacked salmon and trout. The situation became so serious that, on one occasion, 5,000 young fish were transferred from the stew pond at Stockbridge to lakes at Sherfield English, in order to isolate them from River Test water. The condition was treated by making the young fish swim in a dilute solution of the copper salt 'malachite green' before being released from the fish hatcheries into the river. Fortunately, the disease has all but disappeared.

Fishing clubs kept, and still keep, meticulous records of their catches. Every trout and salmon taken from the Test is recorded. Earlier this century a favoured spot for taking large fish was at the point where the Fishlake discharges into the Test at Middlebridge. Here the fish readily accepted the abundance of food supplied by one of the Romsey butchers, who threw waste and offal into the stream. The largest recorded catch at this point was a brown trout weighing 19lb (8.6kg). This is a frequently overlooked example of a positive link between pollution and wild life.

Other Fauna

Otters tend to be nocturnal in their habits and one local fishing club manager only saw one in his fifty years on the river. It was long thought that a single otter could kill thirty or so trout at a time, taking a bite out of each just for the fun of it. There was no hunting with otter hounds locally, though, as generally the otters' main diet was eels. However, they were trapped when they became a menace on the stew ponds. Attempts have been made to reintroduce otters to the Test, but, being very shy creatures, they are frightened away by the activity along the river bank.

Heron were trapped and killed before they became a protected species. All trout farms are festooned with netting to prevent heron from carrying off the product. Like seagulls, **cormorants** are finding their way up the rivers from the sea, and nesting inland.

Mink fur-farms were established in the south of England in the 1940s. Many mink have since escaped or been 'liberated'. Though some have been shot or recaptured, the remainder have bred and killed off many of the moorhens and **voles**. **Coots** do not appear to have been so badly affected. Mink, like otters, have a liking for eels, and have been caught locally trying to raid eel-traps.

Disputes & Legislation

In general, eel migrations down the river to the sea to spawn coincided with salmon migrations up the river for the same purpose. Since the eel-traps prevented salmon swimming upstream, disputes arose between interested parties. One notorious dispute occurred in Romsey between the operator of the Town Mill and Mr Vickers, who owned interests upstream of the Fishlake. The dispute finally went to appeal at the House of Lords. As far as can be ascertained, the Town Mill won.

The British salmon is a renowned traveller. Whereas the Pacific Ocean varieties, such as the Sockeye, die after spawning in the upland streams of North America, the British salmon regularly commutes between the north Atlantic Ocean and its spawning grounds in this country. Owners with fishing interests on the main river have never been keen on salmon disappearing up tributaries during their return migration. One novel way of discouraging adventurous fish was adopted by Lord Palmerston. He had a water-wheel placed in the Fishlake stream at the point where it rejoins the River Test at Middlebridge. The wheel produced no power but the rotating blades prevented salmon swimming up the stream instead of the Test.

During the 19th century there was concern that the development of mills along salmon rivers was increasingly restricting the passage of salmon. Further acts of Parliament were introduced to deal with the problem. In particular, the Salmon Fisheries Act of 1861 sought to stop the decline in the productivity of salmon fisheries by legislating for the installation of fish ladders (passes) at all mills and weirs, and legislating against pollution of salmon rivers and tributaries. Commissioners were to be appointed to monitor the act, and local meetings were to be called to set up representation and monitoring.

The Romsey Register for 1st January, 1862 records a meeting, held at the Town Hall and presided over by Lord Palmerston, 'to confer as to the best steps to be taken for effectual preservation of the fish which make their way up to the River at spawning time'. The River Test Salmon Preservation Society, based at Romsey, was formed later the same year, probably in response to decisions made at the Romsey meeting.

In January 1864, the Inspector of Fisheries sent a questionnaire to Mr Stead, an appointee of this River Test Salmon Preservation Society. Mr Stead was expected to complete the questionnaire and return it. The document included questions about the possible pollution of the river from industrial sites, the condition of fish passes at mills and weirs and the position on fund-raising for the local protection of fish. The Act did not achieve all its objectives, possibly through lack of co-operation, perhaps reflected in the fact that the questionnaire addressed to Mr Stead was never completed and sent back.

Efforts continued, however. A report to a meeting of the Society in 1865 referred to the netting of salmon at the mouth of the Test at Redbridge. This had been having a serious effect on the passage of salmon striving to swim up the river to spawn. A new law sought to redress the problem nationally by banning all fishing at estuaries from noon on Saturdays until 6.00am on Mondays. The presenter of the 1865 report considered that apparent improvements in salmon migration along the River Test were largely due to the efforts of the Society in implementing the provisions of the Act. The Society also had money to provide for a fish ladder to be installed on the Test in Romsey, although there was considerable debate about the efficiency of such contrivances. On a less encouraging note, the meeting was also informed that the funds of the Society were running low.

31

The Secretary and one of the Special Commissioners for English Fisheries visited Romsey in 1871. The same Mr Stead received a letter from them, criticising the state of the fish passes at Testwood, Nursling and Sadler's mills. Although the letter was penned in the most courteous terms, the recipient was left in no doubt as to the opinion of the Commissioners.

Often the miller was committed to keep the mill-stream clear for specified lengths of its course. A late 19th-century agreement for the Abbey Mill required the lessee to 'keep the watercourse from the point at which it leaves the Fishlet Stream near the *Horsefair Brewery* belonging to Messrs Strong & Co. Ltd for the whole length thereof clear and free from filth rubbish & weeds and particularly during the time the water is let out of the Fishlet Stream by the owners thereof during the annual or other cleaning thereof thoroughly clean out the said water course ....'.

Poaching around Romsey was an ever present problem as evidenced by this mid 19th-century notice.

£2 REWARD

WHEREAS

It hath come to the knowledge of the Owners of the

SALMON FISHERY

On the river Test, at Redbridge and Nursling,

That a great number of Kepper or Shidder Salmon, being unseasonable Salmon, Salmon Peal and unsizeable Fish, have been lately unlawfully taken and destroyed in the Branch of the River Test in and about Romsey, and offered for Sale, although the said fish at this Season are unwholesome and unfit for human food, and whereas the Owners of the said Fishery are determined to put a stop to illegal and destructive practices, which renders the offender liable for every such offence to a penalty of £10.

THIS IS TO GIVE NOTICE,

That the above Reward will be given to any person who shall give such evidence as may lead to a Conviction of the offender, on application to Mr. James Haddon, Testwood Mill, Eling; Mr. James Ross; or to Messrs. Stead and Tylee, Solicitors, Romsey.

Romsey, December 26, 1851.

CHIGNELL, PRINTER, BOOKSELLER, BINDER, &c., ROMSEY

The River as a Sewer

At the end of the 20th century most people are sensitive to the effects of pollution, and tend to link it with modern, high-tech industries. There is an inclination to look back on bygone times with nostalgia, associating them with a more tranquil mode of life and a pollution-free environment.

The truth is somewhat different. Surprisingly, the country's first anti-pollution law dates from 1388, following concern over *'maladies and diseases'*, no doubt with minds concentrated by the Black Death, which had not long since ravaged the country. The ground-breaking law was enacted 'for Punishing Nuisances which Cause Corruption of the Air near Cities and Great Towns'. The Act forbade the casting of 'dung, garbage, entrails and other ordure in ditches, rivers, waters and other places'. Those who had already done so were 'to cause them to be utterly removed between this (day) and the feast of St Michael next ensuing after the end of this present Parliament'. The penalty for not complying was a stiff fine '... to lose and forfeit £20 to our Lord the King'.

Legislation piled up over the centuries, mainly aimed at some new pollution associated with the latest technological development, such as mass slaughtering of domestic animals near towns, effluent from tin mining and, most serious of all, the washings from that 19th-century proliferating wonder of civilisation, the gas works.

In Romsey the 18th- and early 19th-century records of the Court Leet bear witness to the lack of regard shown by many of the citizens regarding treatment of the waterways. Although large-scale 19th-century maps show privies dotted along the streams, these were not the only source of pollution within the town. Water has always been an essential requirement for many industrial purposes, and running water a most convenient medium for the disposal of waste products. The invention and development of the water-wheel gradually attracted a range of larger-scale industries. Whatever the process, there would always be waste products, and it was easier to dump these in the river, to be washed downstream, rather than to take the trouble of burning or burying. Chemicals associated with tanning, fulling, dyeing and paper-making were discharged into Romsey's waterways, and even the organic effluent from corn-mills and breweries would have severely upset their ecological balance. These offences aroused widespread protests, but there was always a fine balance between official concern and official need to appease the providers of sound employment.

The Mills in Romsey
in 1866

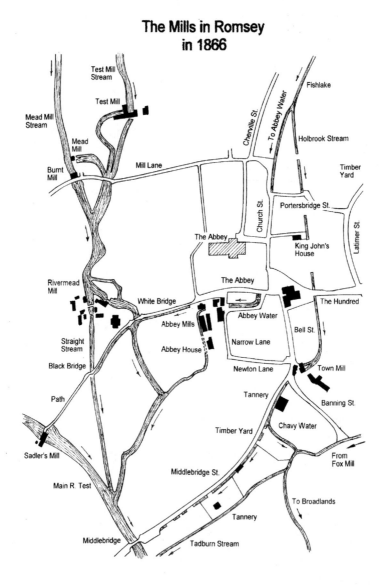

Based upon Ordnance Survey material with the permission of The Controller
of Her Majesty's Stationery Office © Crown Copyright Licence No. MC/98/231

Figure 2
The mills of Romsey, as surveyed in 1866

THE DEVELOPMENT OF ROMSEY'S MILLS

The First Mills

The Domesday Book of 1086 provides the earliest record of mills in Romsey. It states: 'Romsey Abbey holds the whole village in which the Church itself lies ... In lordship 3 mills at 25 shillings ....'. It is uncertain whether a fourth mill, valued at 10s and also held by the Abbey, was one of the three mentioned earlier or an additional mill, but later evidence supports the idea of four mills, or at least four sets of mill-stones. Domesday offers no clue to their location at that time, but ownership then, and throughout the following centuries, cannot be in doubt. Until the dissolution of Romsey Abbey in 1539 all Romsey mills belonged to the Abbess as lord of the manor.

After Domesday, however, some two hundred years have to pass before any further information comes to light about milling in the Romsey area. Then, sometime in the reign of Edward I (1272-1307), the widow of John de Welles made a grant to her grandson, Walter Pansevot. In this grant she passed to him the person of Droco de Assold, miller and one-time serf to her husband. This is the first miller to be known by name in the vicinity of Romsey. Clearly, he was not a free man, and, though other millers of the time may not have been so tightly bound, they probably only won their independence slowly, as leasing became the preferred option for the mill-owners. Droco's master was probably the same John de Welles who was lord of the manor of South Welles, a little to the south of Romsey. There was certainly a mill within this manor by 1444, when mention is made of a mill at Skidmore: if this was already a well-established mill, it may have been the one worked by Droco. No trace now remains of the Skidmore mill, but it does feature briefly in Romsey's milling history, because it was temptingly closer than Romsey's Town Mill for farmers on the southern edge of Romsey Extra.

If Droco de Assold serves as a model for his contemporaries of the 13th century, then the first nameless millers within Romsey itself were at the least direct tenants, if not serfs, of the Abbess. The corn-growers of her extensive manorial holdings were likewise under her thumb, compelled to take their grain to her mills for grinding, even if those mills were not the nearest.

Within Romsey itself, another document from the time of Edward I records a grant made by John le Tapener of Cherville in Romsey to Richard le Bont, dyer, and his wife, Scibilla. One of the witnesses was another dyer, Alexander Tinctor. The grant related to a croft of land enclosed between 'the land of the Abbess of Romsey called "Prestelond" on the south and the water running from the "Holebroke" to the fulling-mill on the north'. This description, though brief, offers many clues. With dyers involved in the grant, and mention of a fulling-mill in the text, the deed strongly suggests that the important woollen-cloth-finishing industry was already well-established in Romsey by the end of the 13th century at least. Furthermore, this document contains the first reference found so far to the upper Holbrook Stream, now more usually known as the Fishlake or Fishlet, and more fully described in the previous chapter about the River Test.

Perhaps most significantly, since 'Prestelond' is a field name that has continued in use, 'the stream running from the Holbrook to the fulling-mill' may be identified as the Horsehead Ditch (see plan of waterways inside back cover). This fed into a major braid of the River Test, now identified as Test Mill Stream. Once the water had done its work in the medieval fulling-mill a route all the way back to the main river would have been necessary. So it is reasonable to suppose that Test Mill Stream was already present at that time, together with its southerly continuation as far as its junction with the main river near Middlebridge. Although this braid has certainly existed for a very long time, there is no way of knowing whether it was created by nature or by man: most probably both contributed to its final form.

In 1420, more than a century after the deed cited above, a lease for a croft called 'le Horsehed' has an almost identical description of the Horsehead Ditch, now said to lead to the Abbess' Mill. It seems likely that the mill in question was the same fulling-mill as in the earlier deed. The Tithe Map of 1845 shows a great swathe of tithe-free land in the relevant area north of Mill Lane, indicating its origins as monastic property, and therefore suggesting that any mill at this location would have belonged to the Abbess.

At the other end of town, south of the raised 'island' on which Romsey was based, another mill was projected in the 1420s. The site for this was on Chavy Water, the one-time boundary marker between Romsey Infra and Romsey Extra. Chavy Water is first mentioned in records of 1313, but more information is provided in 1428, when William Berrell rented from the Abbess a piece of land there, on which to build a new fulling-mill. The rent was to be 4s a year, payable at Michaelmas and Easter. A condition of the lease required him to complete the mill within a year; so, if that condition was fulfilled, Romsey had another fulling-mill by 1429. Unfortunately, nothing more is heard of William Berrell or his mill. Apparently, though, the flow along Chavy Water at that time was considered sufficiently powerful to drive a mill. This adds weight to the earlier suggestion that its present status, as little more than a ditch, is the result of diverting the main flow along the remainder of Middlebridge Street.

1434: Town Mill, Mead Mill and the Mead Mill Stream

In 1434 the Abbess leased to John More of Ashfield two mills at Town Mill and two at 'Medemill', the indication being that in each instance there were two mills, or two sets of mill-stones, under one roof. The rent, to be paid quarterly, was £10 6s 8d plus 450 shafteylings (small eels) and 30 skyvers (large eels), a traditional form of payment. From this time onwards continuity enables both sites to be identified.

The 'two mills at Town Mill' (now the site of the Duke's Mill Shopping Precinct) won their water power from the Holbrook Stream. This man-made stream was already in existence during the reign of Edward I, as has been mentioned earlier. The Town Mill was probably where the inhabitants of the Romsey manors had to bring their corn to be ground, regardless of whether it was their nearest mill or not. The Town Mill was always a corn-mill, even though housing other ancillary activities in more modern times.

Undoubtedly, the Mead Mills were located north of Mill Lane, an area likely to have been one of the earliest mill sites to be developed, for it offered the most easily harnessed source of water-power. A building called Mead Mill, which ceased to operate long ago, still stands back from Mill Lane on the north side; it is now a private museum. This surviving property probably marks the site of the medieval 'Medemill' or Mead Mill. The name, though, may have wandered between it and the nearby Test Mill area, to which it was significantly linked by tithe-free land.

1539: Status at the Dissolution of Romsey Abbey

To summarise: Domesday offers firm evidence that three or four mills existed in Romsey in the 11th century. By 1434 evidence is available for the Holbrook Stream and for double mills at both Town Mill and Mead Mill. There have also been references to two fulling-mills, one receiving water from the Horsehead Ditch and one on Chavy Water, though the latter may not have been built. All these mills belonged to the Abbess who held the Abbey lands and was lord of the manors of Romsey Infra and Romsey Extra until the dissolution of Romsey's nunnery in 1539.

Although successive Abbesses continued throughout this time to control where corn might be ground, a preference for leasing mills to independent individuals gradually evolved. It is impossible to tell whether these lessees were the operating millers, or middle men investing in a sound venture and sub-letting, but some names do suggest a sub-ownership. William Berrell, planning a fulling-mill in Chavy Water in 1428, is an unknown quantity, but John More of Ashfield, who leased four Abbey mills in 1434, is likely to have been landlord to individual millers. He belonged to a family that certainly enjoyed considerable status in later centuries, and the mere act of leasing all four mills suggests a substantial position.

Similarly, ten years later, the name of John Grenefeld was associated with the Town Mill. The Grenefelds were 15th-century lords of the manor of South Wells, to the south of Romsey, where Droco de Assold had milled in Edward I's reign. Although the Town Mill, as ever, continued to be a corn-mill, it is unlikely that John Grenefeld was ever seen with a dusting of flour over him. So, regretfully, it has to be conceded that the actual millers within medieval Romsey must remain anonymous.

The Abbey is Dissolved: Long Live the Abbey Mill

In 1545, just six years after the dissolution of Romsey's Benedictine nunnery, Thomas Thoroughgood and John Foster were granted '... two water-mills called the Towne Milles in Romsey, Hants, with the fishery and land therewith, lately in the tenure of John King and now of Robert Burnham, and other water-mills there viz. the Meade Mylle and le Malte Mille in tenure of John Rysbrygger and a fulling-mill and "le stockes" lately in the tenure of Robert Blose'.

John Foster had been the last Abbey Steward before the dissolution, and acquired a great deal of Abbey property besides the mills. It is safe to assume, therefore, that the new mill-owners had little involvement in the actual running of their properties. At last, though, references to some probable millers - John King, Robert Burnham, John Rysbrygger and Robert Blose - do emerge alongside the new owners' names.

It is noticeable that, in the 1545 grant to Thoroughgood and Foster, Town Mill and Mead Mill are once again mentioned by name. In respect of Mead Mill, it suggests that there was a corn-mill, a malt-mill and a fulling-mill on or near the site, reinforcing suspicion that this was a busy industrial area. Such multiplicity of uses was not unusual. What is unusual is that, throughout the whole period of the Abbess' jurisdiction, there has been no mention of the Abbey Mill. This stood on the southern perimeter of the Abbey precinct and was fed by Abbey Water.

Traditionally, Abbey Mill has been considered to be the site of one of the Domesday mills, but recent research has cast doubt on this idea. In 1546 Henry VIII granted the southern precinct of the dissolved Romsey Abbey to Messrs Bellowe and Biggett. In this deed details of the defunct Abbey precinct are given; they include 'still waters' in the area of Abbey Water but no water-mill. Bellowe and Biggett were not local men but, seemingly, a pair of entrepreneurs who acquired monastic land throughout the country, and quickly sold it on. By 1551 the Romsey Abbey precinct was in the hands of Sir Francis Fleming. In that year Sir Francis granted a lease of property including the same part of the Abbey. This time, however, the deed clearly describes a water-mill beyond Abbey Water. It probably stood more or less where the archway now leads from Abbey Water into the road called The Abbey. So far no reference to an Abbey mill has been found prior to this lease of 1551.

In 1586 William and Jane Fleming of Broadlands made a deed, by which they conveyed property to the St Barbe family. William was the son of Sir Francis Fleming; his wife, Jane, was the daughter of John Foster, the last Abbey Steward; and Broadlands was the estate created out of the Abbey farmlands on the southern edge of Romsey. Amongst the property conveyed to the St Barbe family, who succeeded the Flemings at Broadlands, was the old monastic site, including the mill first mentioned in 1551. Thus Abbey Mill became vested in the Broadlands estate, and subsequent mill-owners of the Tudor mill, and its successor, were only leaseholders.

After 1551, though, no more is heard of Abbey Mill *per se* until 1708 when Thomas May took the lease of the site from Sir James St Barbe, then owner of Broadlands. In 1731, after the death of Sir James St Barbe, his heir, Humphrey Sydenham of Somerset, negotiated the surrender of the 1708 lease. He granted Thomas May a new 31-year lease in its place; the rent was to be £27 per annum. This new lease referred to 'All that piece or parcel of waste ground containing 13 luggs of land, late in occupation of Thomas May and now staked out and measured ... and being in a place known by the name of the Abbey yard and adjoining to the mills and head with the piece of ground between the two watercourses ...... where late stood a mill called Abbey Mill and now a stable and part of the buildings of the said mill, with

39

liberty to erect a mill or mills and other buildings thereon ....'. With minor provisos Thomas was given permission to pull down old buildings and erect new ones; it is conjectured that the new mill was just to the west, or north-west, of the old Tudor one. The permission for changes was probably partly retrospective; a 1708 document concerning a nearby property refers to 'the way leading from the Market Place ... to the place where the Abbey Mill formerly stood'. Such a retrospective element to the 1731 lease would also account for the claim made in a much later document of 1807 that '... the mill was set up by the Grandfather of the present Mays about the year 1708'. This 1807 statement, made when the mill was owned by James May, makes it clear that the mill was a corn-mill.

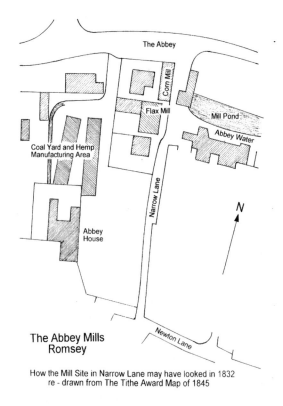

The Abbey Mills
Romsey

How the Mill Site in Narrow Lane may have looked in 1832
re - drawn from The Tithe Award Map of 1845

Figure 3: Plan of Abbey Mill

After a century, the May family ended its link with Abbey Mill soon after the beginning of the 1800s. The Mays were then succeeded by William Lintott. It was probably Mr Lintott, who, sometime between 1813 and 1822, built a flax-mill next to the corn-mill on a north-south alignment. It is difficult now to ascertain which was the site of the May's corn-mill and which the new flax-mill. An advertisement of 1832 leaves no doubt that there were, at that time, both a corn-mill 'in full trade' and a flax-mill 'three storeys high adjoining the corn-mill'. Unfortunately, it is still not clear from the advertisement which mill was which. Uncertainties remain, but the balance of probabilities is that

40

the corn-mill occupied the northern site on Figure 3, whilst the later flax-mill was built on the southern site, probably on freehold land. This is the way the two mills are labelled on Figure 3. For some decades it is thus necessary to refer to Abbey Mills in the plural.

Abbey Mills were supplied by the westerly branch of the Fishlake Stream that had brought water to the nunnery precinct in the medieval period. As described in the first chapter, two separate streams carried the water from the adjacent sites back to the River Test. From the southern mill site a stream still flows under and across the grounds of La Sagesse Convent to join the combined waters from the Mead and Test Mills by the eastern corner of the Memorial Park diamond. The other, Coleman's Ditch, which was probably the tail water from the corn-mill on the northern site, flows westwards towards the Town Memorial Park to join the Mead/Test Mill Stream by the White Bridge.

The fact that both streams from the Abbey Mills flow into the tail waters from the Mead and Test Mills does suggest that the latter sites, to the north of Mill Lane, were established first. It is also interesting that the rights and responsibilities for the full length of the Fishlake/Holbrook Stream, from its beginnings at Greatbridge to its junction with the Test, were vested in the owner of the Town Mill. Ownership of the Abbey Mills only entailed responsibility for the westerly branch from the point of separation north of Portersbridge Street. Again the implication is that Abbey Mill was created at a later date. Although it may be overturned by future research, this proposition must be considered seriously in the light of current evidence.

The flax-mill had ceased to operate by 1865, and the Abbey Mills site reverted to a single mill. There is evidence that by 1867 the more modern southern site was being used as a corn-mill. By that time the property was owned by Henry Wheable, who also had an interest in Greatbridge Mill. He leased Abbey Mill to various millers, who probably had a number of employees. The census return of 1851, for which everyone had to give a job description, is the first record to give a reasonably wide view of the individual work-titles within the mills. The miller's foreman, miller's carter and miller's apprentice may have worked in this or one of the other corn-mills.

By 1872 '... all that piece of land whereon then or lately stood the Abbey Mill ....' had been transferred to the Trustees of The Abbey Congregational

Church (now the United Reformed Church). Also '... in pursuance of the indenture the mill etc. had been pulled down and a schoolhouse then used as classrooms ... had been erected on the site thereof ....'. These classrooms, opened in 1873, still stand on the northern site where the May corn-mill is thought to have been. This sequence endorses the suggestion that the flax-mill on the southern site had closed around 1865, and had been converted for use as a corn-mill by 1867. It would then have left the defunct corn-mill on the northern site available for sale; this was then pulled down to make way for the classrooms.

From 1867 the story is straightforward. The surviving, more modern, mill continued in use as a corn-mill until 1925, when it burned down. A new single storey building was then erected on the original foundations for use as part of the adjacent convent of the Sisters of La Sagesse, who had established St Joseph's orphanage for boys in 1888. The new building, with a semi-circular projection surmounted by a dome and a cross, survives and can now be recognised at the junction of Abbey Water and Narrow Lane.

The Town Mill in Secular Hands

John Foster, steward to the last Abbess at the dissolution of Romsey Abbey, maintained his link with the Town Mill perhaps longer than he might have wished. When Robert Burnham died in 1554, one of his bequests referred to the Town Mill 'lying to mortgage to me by one John Foster of Baddesley'. Robert's wife, Bettrixe, inherited this interest and four years later bequeathed it to her son.

The mill later came into the possession of Edward Hooper, a Dorset landowner. When he sold it to Ambrose Grove and John Wise of Romsey in 1679, the property was described as 'two wheat mills and one malt-mill in the same millhouse situate in Romsey'.

By the mid-18th century the May family had entered the scene. Described as a 'mealman' either Thomas May the elder, or his son, Thomas the younger, bought a half interest from the descendants of the Grove and Wise partnership in 1760. When Thomas the younger died in 1796 he left 'All that my half part of those water corn or grist-mills called Town Mills ....' to John and Charles May. He also bequeathed over £2,000 to be shared between his four daughters, so was clearly a man of substance. Another member of the family, James May, was at the Abbey Mill.

The May family owned or leased mills in Romsey for nearly two hundred years. It is possible that, from the beginning, they were well-to-do investors, knowledgeable about milling but personally more involved in the finances and improvement of the machinery than in day-to-day milling. Indeed, during the fifty years that the family worked both Town Mill and Abbey Mill, there were probably times when the family needed a manager at one of the mills at least. If the comfortable wealth reflected in the will of Thomas May junior is considered, then it is unlikely that he was the operating miller.

The affluence of the Mays became conspicuously noticeable after 1815, when the business was taken over by Joseph May, an incoming member of the family 'from Birmingham where he had made a good fortune as a jeweller'. He was able to purchase the Town Mill outright by 1836, completely buying out the heirs of Grove and Wise. By this purchase he acquired not only the mill house and the mills but also 'streams, waters, watercourses, milldams, floodgates, hatchways and fenders proceeding from and situate between the piles on an island near Greatbridge called the Point otherwise Dowlestakes and the said Mills and from the Mills as the water course runneth to Middlebridge'.

For the next thirty years Joseph May had a succession of millers running operations. He physically distanced himself from the mill, living on the outskirts of Romsey on the road to Winchester. His home, now called Chirk Lodge, still stands just below Romsey Hospital. One link with the May's ownership of the Town Mill was never severed, though. An island at Greatbridge is still called May's Island, another one Smaller May's Island.

Figure 4: Duke's (Town) Mill from the south-east
by Val Grace

Towards the end of the 19th century the May family gave up control of the Town Mill. Mr Edward Meddings, who had been milling at Greatbridge Mill, bought the property, which included meadow land near Greatbridge, May's Island and Smaller May's Island, and 1½ miles of the Fishlake Stream extending from these islands to Middlebridge. The ownership of the stream entitled him to rent from other property owners who needed to cross his stream to reach their own property. The last owners of the Town Mill, James Duke & Sons, milled there until it closed in the late 1960s. The disused mill buildings burned down in 1970, and in their place the Duke's Mill Shopping Precinct was built. It was not until the 1990s that the local authority, needing to build a bridge entrance into the historic King John's Garden, eventually purchased the stream from Mr Duke.

Sadler's Mill on the Main River Test.

Another mill first mentioned early in the 16th century is Sadler's Mill, though the site may well have been used prior to its appearance in records. Sadler's Mill is probably the best known of Romsey's surviving mills; it seems to have been the only Romsey mill to be developed on the main course of the River Test. Its ownership was long linked with the lord of the manor of Great and Little Spursholt, to the north, with variants of the spelling, such as Sparshott, Spurshott or Spurshot, being given to the mill over the centuries. The names of actual millers have not been found for the Tudor period.

Richard Benger, owner of the manor of Great and Little Spursholt, died in 1529. Seventeen years later his widow sold the property to John Dowse. The sale included a fishery on the River Test and a water-mill used as a tucking-mill (another name for a fulling-mill). How long the mill had existed prior to 1546 is not known. John Dowse died in 1557 leaving his property to his eldest son, Richard. The bequest included the mill, believed to be on or near the site now occupied by Sadler's Mill.

Information for this period has come from records about a lengthy milling dispute that is more fully detailed in a later section of this chapter, 'Trouble At T'Mill'. An interesting paragraph in one of the dispute documents, dated 1579, claims that diverting the water away from the main channel was 'to the great annuisance and utter destruction as well of those who are ownours and Fearmours of the said mylls standinge upon the auncient Channel of the said Ryver by reason of Divertinge of the said Water whereby the said mylls are not able to grinde nor to full for want of water'. This suggests that there was more than one mill on the main channel and that both a fulling-mill and a corn-mill were present. No other separate site of a major nature has been identified on the main river. It may be that, as in later centuries, there was a secondary activity at Sadler's Mill from an early time.

There are no definite clues to explain the name 'Sadler's', or when it replaced the earlier Spursholt name, but the Hearth Tax Returns of 1665 raise an intriguing point. Only two properties are recorded for the parish of Spursholt. One is listed as being the farm of that name; it boasted eight hearths suggesting a sizeable property, which may have started life as the manor house. The other property had one hearth and was in the possession of Richard Sadler. Perhaps he was the miller at that time, living in a cottage at nearby Spursholt and, in local parlance at least, giving his own name to the mill. It is the closest indication so far found to explain the name of Sadler's Mill. Unfortunately for this slender link, official use of 'Sadler's' has not been found in legal documents before the late 18th century.

There is a time-lapse before further news of Sadler's Mill appears in 1718, when Samuel Partiger sold it to William Horne and Andrew Martin, price £680. Samuel Partiger had married one of the descendants of Richard Dowse, the plaintiff way back in 1579, so there may have been long continuity of ownership. In 1745 Andrew Martin sold the mill, by then described as a grist (grain) mill, to the first Lord Palmerston for £1,150; it really had been a profitable enterprise. The active millers are more readily identified after this time.

Lord Palmerston, who had bought Broadlands in 1736, erected the present mill building. The Broadlands accounts for 1747 itemise 'leather for pumps, beer for the workmen, nails, spikes and bricks (24,000 for £18) and a working millstone'. The building was finished in 1748 at a total cost of £1,709, a considerable investment, and leased to Benjamin Baker for 14 years at an annual rent of £70. At this time the first reference is made to an oil-and-skin (leather-dressing) mill, situated near the grist-mill but on the east side of the main river and with its own cut, or watercourse. This mill also became Lord Palmerston's property. It is possible that the leather dressed at this mill was chamois leather, prepared by pounding cod liver oil into sheepskin, one of the preferred skins for this purpose. In support of this there is mention of drying sheds and lime pits nearby; lime pits could have been used for the removal of any residual wool from the sheepskin. Interestingly, the old cloth fulling-mills could easily have been used to prepare chamois leather, the same machinery being used to pound the oil into the skin. If the oil-and-skin mill east of Sadler's grist-mill did utilise the old cloth-fulling technology, the work may have taken place on the site of the old Tudor fulling-mill, assuming that the latter did indeed co-exist with a grist-mill, as suggested earlier.

In 1777 the ownership of Sadler's Mill changed again, as Benjamin Dawkins bought the grist-mill and had the present mill-house built. Rather arbitrarily, the name 'Sadler's' appears in legal documents from this date. Mrs Elizabeth Baker, widow (presumably of the earlier owner), later bought the oil-and-skin mill; there was an arrangement to use the water alternately with the corn-mill, if the supply was insufficient. Later, she and her son, Charles, who was a breeches maker, worked the leather mill until Charles became bankrupt at the end of the century.

At the beginning of the 19th century both the corn-mill (advertised in 1811 as having two water-wheels) and the oil-and-skin mill were in the possession of John Dawkins, son of Benjamin. Both mills were heavily mortgaged, a situation that was to occur regularly in the following years. On the death of John Dawkins, both corn and leather mills were sold by his brother, Thomas, to their relatives, the Fishes of Spursholt Farm. When James Fish died in 1834, he left all his property to his sons, John and Henry, with the condition that his wife, Phoebe, should receive the rents of the leather mill. This inheritance passed to their daughter, also Phoebe, who married Charles Jewell of Romsey, sack manufacturer. Phoebe and Charles had one son, christened with names to cover all generations and families - Benjamin Dawkins Fish Jewell. He turned his back on milling, and departed to London to become a policeman.

'Burt's Mill'

By the middle of the 19th century the small oil-and-skin mill had fallen into disuse; for a short while in the 1850s it became a sawmill. By 1865, though, it was reported that 'these erections were some time since pulled down and the cut stopped up'. The corn mill had been put up for public auction in 1846, when it was bought by an entrepreneur, William Tripp, for £1,700. He made some improvements and then sold it to a miller from Dorset, Aine Burt, for £2,050. Mr Burt's son, Charles, was already working at the grist-mill. Locally, the family name became linked so closely with the mill that photographs of the scene often bear the caption 'Burt's Mill'. The Burt family, however, were unable to meet debt obligations to their mortgagee, William Jeffery. In 1889, after Mr Jeffery's death, the Hon. Evelyn Ashley of Broadlands bought the mill, now driving six pairs of stones. Sadler's Mill thus returned to the Broadlands estate just over a hundred years after the second Lord Palmerston had sold it, and remains a part of the estate to this day.

The Burt family, though no longer the owners, continued to operate the mill through into the beginning of the 20th century; then from about 1913 until 1932 the miller was W. Holloway. The previous name of Sadler's Mill was re-instated in the locality. In its final days of active life, the mill was used to power the dynamo providing electricity at Broadlands. It ceased to operate altogether in 1968, though both the mill and the mill-house still stand, and may yet have a future.

Rivermead Mill (Abbey Mill 2)

Rivermead is a short distance west of Romsey Abbey. As the need for more power arose, the possibility of creating another mill in the Rivermead area must have been recognised, for it was in the path of the waterway that took the combined tail races of Mead, Burnt and Test mills back to the main river. But no mention of a mill on this site is available before 1683 when it crops up in a legal case reported by Dr Latham, an early recorder of Romsey's history, who wrote between the 1790s and 1830s. 'It appears that the Straight Stream from Mr Sharp's Paper-mills, emptying itself into the main River Test between the Principal Stream and the small one to the East, was made about the year 1683 but by whom is not certain.' The 'straight stream' still runs, nowadays between houses.

It would appear that some form of paper-making was always at the heart of milling on the Rivermead site. At the time that Dr Latham was writing, in the early 1800s, William Sharp owned the paper-mill in Rivermead. The Sharps were prominent in many aspects of Romsey life through the 18th and early 19th century. They were involved in banking, upholstery and auctioneering, as well as paper-making. Their origins, the places where they lived in Romsey and some of their hobbies are known; some played an active part in the civic and social life of the town. At Rivermead Mill the paper-making branch of the family produced writing paper for several decades. Examples of their paper with the watermark 'SS' for Stephen Sharp or 'WS' for William Sharp, and bearing dates between the late 1700s and early 1800s, have been found in collections of old Romsey documents.

As elsewhere, the post-Napoleonic era was a time of economic failure for many Romsey businessmen, and William Sharp became bankrupt in 1830. Following his downfall Rivermead was the scene of a succession of short-lived enterprises, mostly linked to some degree with paper-making and detailed in the chapter about the uses of the Romsey's mills. In the same chapter is also information about a more successful mid-19th-century undertaking on the multiple-use site, namely sawmilling. Then, towards the end of the 19th century, Rivermead eventually found its feet again with the leatherboard industry, which lasted to the 1960s. William Williams and his son, Lewis, were largely responsible for this period at Rivermead.

Some Romsonians still recall the hierarchical atmosphere that pervaded 20th-century mill-work, certainly at Rivermead. Employees there did not enter their work-place from the mill house end of the site. Instead, they were expected to walk round to Mill Lane and enter from there, a long way round but one that was considered more suitable to their status.

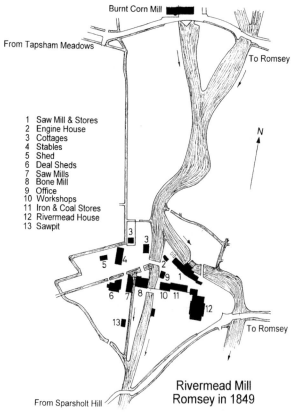

1 Saw Mill & Stores
2 Engine House
3 Cottages
4 Stables
5 Shed
6 Deal Sheds
7 Saw Mills
8 Bone Mill
9 Office
10 Workshops
11 Iron & Coal Stores
12 Rivermead House
13 Sawpit

Rivermead Mill
Romsey in 1849

Re-drawn from a Plan made by J.D.Doswell & Son 1849

Figure 5: Plan of Rivermead Mill, 1849

An excellent plan of the whole Rivermead site was drawn in 1849, when the mill was offered for sale during one of its difficult periods. It shows two distinct mill buildings, one on the eastern branch and one on the Straight Stream. It seems reasonable to propose that the mill on the eastern leg would have been built first, since it was on a stream carrying water away from the medieval Mead Mill. This would suggest that the site may have been developed before 1683 for some yet unknown purpose. With this eastern leg in place, together with its hatches and high-level head-water, it seems a simple step to join the

48

third side of the triangle with the Straight Stream, and so create another mill on the site. Subsequently, all mills on this complex, whatever their purpose, went under the name of 'Abbey Mills'. The problem of having two Romsey mill sites both named 'Abbey Mills' has been avoided by using the location name of Rivermead for the later one.

North of Mill Lane: Test Mill, Burnt Mill & Mead Mill

The comparatively recent confusion about the use of the name 'Abbey Mills' is a timely reminder that, in medieval times, the name of 'Mead Mill' may have moved around in the area to the north of Mill Lane, where so much of Romsey's early milling seems to have been situated. The later history of this prime milling area is confusing in another way.

Test Mill stood at the end of the road now called Hollman Drive, once just a gated track off the north side of Mill Lane. Formal use of the name, 'Test Mill', seems to date only from the 19th century, whilst the history of the mill prior to the mid-18th century is surprisingly elusive. Yet it stood on a site with the most promising potential in terms of natural water-power.

The suitability of this site for milling purposes makes it highly likely that, despite a singular lack of specific identification, it was one of the locations used in medieval times. The theory of Test Mill's early origins is re-inforced not only by its proximity to Mead Mill and its situation on tithe-free land, but also by evidence about Romsey's mills given for the 1807 dispute. A statement made at that time indicates that the mill had been rebuilt in the 1760s, with three wheels for a large 'paper manufactory', noting that beforehand there had been only one small wheel for a tucking-mill. It would be reasonable to suggest that this tucking, or fulling, mill had been established during the high period of the medieval cloth-finishing industry. It may even have been a direct descendant of the late 13th-century fulling-mill to which the Horsehead Ditch led in the time of Edward I. (The Horsehead Ditch feeds into Test Mill Stream; *see plan of waterways inside back cover*.)

Perhaps all the mills that developed north of Mill Lane had previously shared a common identity, known collectively as Mead Mills. This would explain the lack of individual names for the various activities on this stretch of land.

An additional 'fulling' mill north of Test Mill has caused extra confusion for researchers. The first clear evidence for this little mill is found in the Land

49

Tax Assessment of 1800; it was set in just 12 perches of land (about one thirteenth of an acre). The owner was then James Sharp, with Thomas Munday as tenant. James Sharp was a manufacturer of Shalloon, a sort of woollen cloth, and Thomas Munday was probably working for him. By 1810 the mill had passed into the hands of the Skeats paper-making family. Within four years it was advertised as 'a newly erected fulling mill with a half-stuff engine', 'half-stuff' being half-made paper pulp, and it had clearly been incorporated into the paper-making business. Once again, cloth-fulling techniques seem to have been transferred to the paper industry, apparently in a totally rebuilt mill, identified as 'New Mill' on Figure 6.

By 1847 Test Mill was being advertised as 'a double paper-mill formerly a paper-mill and fulling-mill nearby adjacent'. The fulling section was the '12 perch' mill just to the north of the main one; it was now known as Spratt's Mill. Any doubts about which site was the earlier one, Test Mill or Spratt's Mill, are easily resolved. The little mill was supplied from a high water level retained by the weirs and hatches of the main mill, on which its existence was totally dependent. It must, therefore, have been developed after Test Mill, and perhaps had not existed for very long before its first known mention in 1800. Spratt's Mill seems to have closed by the early 1850s.

After the rebuilding of the 1760s, Test Mill played an important part in Romsey's paper-making industry under a succession of owners, more fully described below under 'Dynasties of the Paper-mills'. The mill underwent further major alterations at the end of the 19th century during the ownership of William Harvey. Although paper-making at Test Mill ceased in 1939, the mill, known for a few decades as *Drayton's Mill*, was rebuilt yet again in 1947. Nevertheless, it appears not to have recovered its earlier impetus until taken over in 1962 by John Busby. He successfully ran the mill as a factory producing expanded polystyrene packaging; and then, after retiring in 1976, he leased the premises to light engineering companies. Following Mr Busby's death in 1994, Test Mill was demolished in 1997 to make way for a residential development.

The new development fittingly preserves a memory of the mill's history. The plaque that had first been imbedded in the wall of the Harvey mill building has been reset into the new property. Intriguingly, it reads 'James Skeats 1706; William Harvey 1897', which suggests a much longer paper-making story for the mill than documents have been able to support so far.

Finally, the last owner of Test Mill, John Busby, has been remembered by the creation of a small public memorial garden near the old mill site. This has been named The Busby Garden, and features a stone engraved 'in loving memory of John Busby, MBE, owner of *Test Mill Factory*, 1962-1994'.

Burnt Mill was a corn-mill very close to the medieval Mead Mill, but seemingly of much later date. Though both took water from the same stream, it is thought that the short link to Burnt Mill was a later cut. This mill presents different problems for the researcher, because many documents give the impression that Burnt Mill and Mead Mill were alternative names for the same mill. It is possible that the 'Burnt' name was applied initially to Mead Mill after a fire, but then was eventually settled on the newer mill, which, though a quite separate operation, shared a common curtilage with the older mill.

Fronting directly onto the north side of Mill Lane, Burnt Mill can only be dated back to the early 1700s. The milling dispute document of 1807 suggests that it was rebuilt by William Card around 1753 with two water-wheels 'to grind corn and work dressing and hoisting tackle at the same time'. Prior to William Card's rebuilding of Burnt Mill it had been 'a small Grist-mill worked in succession by Segar, Hart and Martin', but for how long before that time is uncertain.

Mead Mill had to change to survive in the 18th century, when the days of Romsey's high prosperity as a cloth-finishing centre had ended. Until 1756 it still had a small 'tucking' wheel, though the machinery was used for leather-dressing rather than the earlier cloth-fulling. Then, a fire of 1756 meant that Mead as well as Burnt Mill had to be rebuilt during the 1750s, offering a splendid opportunity for a change of use. Whilst the fulling stocks at the little mill east of Sadler's Mill seem to have been adapted to leather work, the new Mead Mill was dedicated to the increasingly fashionable and successful paper industry. In this transition Romsey was following a widespread trend in similar small towns, and the clear water that had served the fulling of cloth was equally suitable for paper-making.

Mead Mill was fed by the Mead Mill Stream. Its tail water joined into the tail water from Test Mill site, and both waters still flow together along the same common route back to the main river. Interestingly, the water-wheel pit of Mead Mill is now occupied by a fine eel-trap. Eels are still caught, but it is no longer necessary to render a portion of the catch to the Abbess.

Dynasties of the Paper-mills

The story of the ownership and operation of the paper-mills is a particularly tortuous one, as some families occupied more than one mill, sometimes successively, sometimes concurrently, and the picture is far from clear. The repetition of identical family names adds to the confusion, as do 'sleeping partners' and mortgagees.

The earliest paper-makers known for Romsey are John Hockley senior, and Matthew Plyer, mentioned in 1712 and 1715 respectively. As the Rivermead site appears to have been the only one making paper at that time, it may be assumed that both were associated with that mill, though whether as partners or employer/employee is quite unknown. The information about John Hockley only reveals that he lived in Latimer Street, but Matthew Plyer is said to be a paper-maker 'near the Abbey': the nearness to the Abbey must mean Rivermead Mill. John Hockley junior would appear to own this mill in the 1730s, but later he bought Mead Mill, having 'previously erected a paper-mill on the site of the burnt down fulling-mill'. As this rebuilding appears to have taken place following the fire of 1756, he may have overlapped at both Mead and Rivermead, since he was being assessed for poor law payments in respect of Rivermead until 1762. Likewise, there is uncertainty about William Sharp, described as a 'master paper-maker' in 1770. Although the Sharp family was generally linked with Rivermead, this William may have been working at Mead Mill, for a while at least.

The names of several paper-makers are known for the early period of the industry, but their status and place of work are far from clear. There are long gaps concerning the occupants of the various paper-mills, and it is only towards the end of the 1700s that more consistent connections may be made. Then, William Sharp (perhaps successor to William the 'master paper-maker') was primarily associated with Rivermead Mill and James Skeats with Test Mill. Mead Mill, from 1790 at least, was occupied by Henry Skeats, and from 1793 by the partnership of Godfrey and Skeats. A fire in 1793 necessitated another rebuilding. When the rebuilt mill was offered for sale, in 1800, Godfrey and Skeats were still in occupation, but shortly afterwards it was purchased by Edward Jones, a Romsey butcher, who presumably saw it as an investment. Under his ownership paper-making continued at Mead Mill until 1830 at least; but by 1832 Edward Jones had given up, and his mill was offered for sale.

These were difficult times for paper-makers; only a few years earlier there had been a strike by journeymen paper-makers for 'an advance on wages', and in 1830 William Sharp at Rivermead Mill had become bankrupt. The bankruptcy document recalls that 'Wm. Sharp did seek and endeavour to get his living by the buying of rags, smelts, indigo and other articles ... converting the same into paper and selling the same'. The inclusion of indigo suggests that he was making blue wrapping paper, often called sugar paper. This may indicate a dwindling of the Sharp's previous involvement in the white paper business. Dated watermarks in surviving Romsey documents certainly suggest that use of local white paper diminished after the 1820s.

Meanwhile, Test Mill had continued paper-making under the direction of the Skeats family. The paper-mill was advertised in 1814 as 'a two-vat mill' and emphasised 'a superior spring of water independent of the stream for washing rags'. This was clearly an important feature, as white paper was being manufactured there. As with the Sharp family at Rivermead, the Skeats' Test Mill paper was distinctively watermarked. Amongst old Romsey documents, papers have been found with 'IJ&T Skeats 1801', 'Skeats 1815' and 'Skeats 1817'. Another watermark records the entry of a partner into the business, namely Mr Brookman, as in 'Brookman and Skeats 1816'.

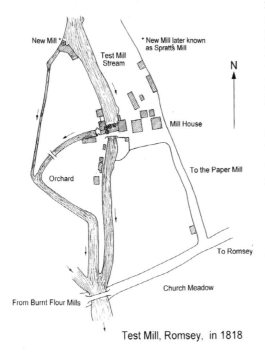

Test Mill, Romsey, in 1818

Re-drawn from a Plan made by J.Doswell
for Mr. Wm. Brookman, January 1818

Figure 6: Plan of Test Mill, 1818

The Skeats' paper-making dynasty seems to have ended between 1816 and 1818, since watermarks featuring only the Brookman name have been found on paper for 1819. William Brookman was then associated with the mill for many years, and it was he who built the very fine house, Test House, nearby.

It is not known precisely when Mr Brookman left Test Mill, but he was there for over forty years. The last available reference to him appears in Kelly's Directory for 1859. In 1862 the mill was not in use, but by 1866 it was being run by William Harvey. It was Harvey who, in 1897, recorded his and the Skeats name in a plaque set into a wall during alterations. Perhaps as a result of this building work, he ran into financial difficulties and committed suicide in 1900. His son, also William, continued to run the mill, and was still there in 1917, with one 60-inch machine. The mill was then reported to be making nine tons of paper per week from rags, ropes, etc.

The Hockleys, Sharps and Skeats, moving around Romsey's three paper-mills, have made a positive, if confusing, mark on the town's history, but there were many others who contributed to a greater or lesser extent. Over time the paper-mills offered employment to a wide range of skilled and unskilled artisans, and may be considered one of the major local employers. In the 1851 census John Jones was listed as a paper-cutter. Amongst the paper-makers in this record was a lone woman, Emily Long, but paper-sorters on the other hand seem to have been exclusively female. These few people must represent two centuries of paper-workers, some known by name but most with a question mark over their precise status and place of work.

Greatbridge Mill
A reference to this mill appears in a document of 27th April 1691, in which Mary Merser of Greatbridge Mill, Romsey, widow, assigned the lease of 'two water-mills under one roof' to Anthony Hyde, yeoman, of Stanbridge, Romsey, for the remainder of a term of 99 years commencing 17th September 1685. The link with the manor of Stanbridge, to the north of Romsey, is one that persists over the years, tending to draw Greatbridge Mill away from Romsey town.

The mill took its water from the River Test along a leat running parallel to the main river. After doing useful work in the mill the water returned back into the same river further downstream. Greatbridge Mill appears always to have been a corn-mill.

In the 18th century, through the Fifield family, the ownership was linked with both Stanbridge and the neighbouring manor of Roke, but in the middle of the 19th century it was sold to Joshua Withers, one of a large and long-established Romsey family. His son, George, became the miller, remaining there for some 25 years. It would seem that at about this time the house on the island near to the mill became a separate property known as The Island, subsequently referred to as 'formerly Greatbridge Cottage'.

The mill became the property of Thomas Aylward of Lockerly in 1880, and was leased to Edward Meddings, who later took over the Town Mill. Milling at Greatbridge seems to have stopped about a hundred years ago.

Interdependence
The interlinking network of streams carrying water to and from all the mills so far encountered means that they were, to a greater or lesser extent, interdependent. Whilst there is no way to be sure about what happened in the early days, or how the watercourses may have been altered during the intervening years, the sequence of their development, as hazarded above, appears to be at least plausible.

Fox Mill on the Tadburn Stream
The remaining mill, Fox Mill, was a corn-mill. It has been considered last because it enjoyed a semi-independent existence, distant from the network that linked the other mills and with a much more recent history. Now skirted by the Romsey by-pass, it was originally called The Hundred Mill, because it was then approached by a long entrance from the street to the north called The Hundred. Subsequently, it was also known as Soffe's Mill and Arnold's Mill after 19th-century owners. It probably took its final name from the Fox Inn that once stood slightly further south on the old road to Southampton (now a private road within Broadlands Park).

The lease for the site was only concluded in 1799 and was made between William Jesser, millwright, and John Fleming, at that time Lord of the Manor of Romsey Extra. It differs from the other mills in that it was built on the Tadburn Stream, an east-west running tributary of the Test. It was, therefore, quite separate from the other mills, which totally depended on water from the River Test itself.

It seems unlikely, however, that the Fox Mill site would have been considered viable before the Andover-Redbridge Canal was completed in the mid-1790s with Romsey a key staging point on its route. It is doubtful whether the flow down the Tadburn Stream would have been sufficient to drive the mill without the overflow it received from the canal. Indeed, a document of 1893 refers to a statement by Robert Arnold, miller at Fox Mill, reporting that 'Mr Arnold states that the Fox Mill was originally driven by water from the Tadburn Stream and from waste water from the old canal'. (As the canal was fed by the River Test, Fox Mill cannot be considered to be totally independent of the main river.)

Even with the addition of water from the canal, continued and even augmented after the canal closed, the mill always struggled for power. Some of its efforts to overcome the problems are covered in the next chapter, 'Water-Wheels and Water-Power'. Fox Mill was destroyed by fire c1890, after which it was sold to the Broadlands estate. Even though it was rebuilt soon afterwards, and served for various industrial uses, it never worked as a corn-mill again.

Surviving Buildings

Although the mills are now all closed, and their sites mostly redeveloped, some buildings survive, mainly the millers' houses. Sadler's Mill is probably the most complete of all the mill complexes. There, both the 18th-century corn-mill and the adjoining mill-house enhance the pleasure of the riverside walk at the 'Salmon Leap'. In the town centre, the last, and impressively large, mill-house for the vanished Town Mill still stands on the corner of Broadwater Road, though only the facade is now original. Houses associated with the Abbey Mills may be seen at the top of Narrow Lane and through the gateway of La Sagesse Convent. Further west, and nearly opposite the entrance to the Town Memorial Park, Rivermead House stands in splendid glory, although much rebuilt after a serious fire in the 1920s. A vivid account of life in Rivermead House during the early 1900s was written by Mrs A. Wellington and published in LTVAS *Pots & Papers, Vol. 5.*

On the southern edge of town, near the roundabout by the public entrance to Broadlands House, Fox Mill still straddles the Tadburn Stream. On the far northern edge, the privately owned Greatbridge Mill, now the offices for a trout farm, is lovingly cared for, despite having ceased working nearly 100 years ago.

Last, but by no means least, the Mead Mill area still offers a range of buildings. To the left of the entrance to Mill Lane Water Gardens is Burnt Mill (now rebuilt as a private house) with its neighbouring Burnt Mill House. Within the Water Gardens is the old Mead Mill with its eel-trap, now a private museum. Finally, at the end of Hollman Drive, although the mill itself has been replaced by a new development, Test House still stands as testimony to the success of William Brookman, paper-maker.

'Trouble at T'Mill': Disputes about Water Power

Problems about the waterways arose from the conflicting agricultural, domestic and industrial uses of water from the Test, or, more dramatically, between the owners of various mills competing for the same power source. The network of streams gave space and opportunity for a growing number of mills, but there was essentially only one finite source of water, the River Test.

Most of these milling disputes seem to date from the 18th century, when more sophisticated technology, together with the expansion and conversion of individual mills and the general proliferation of mill sites, placed excessive demands on the water-flow. Nevertheless, the first recorded problems date from Tudor times. Mill-owners, millers and their workers and hirelings were all involved.

The Tudor dispute centred on Sadler's Mill, which Richard Dowse had inherited from his father in 1557. Richard had trouble with his milling neighbours; in 1573 he found it necessary to petition the Rt Hon. Sir Raphe Sadler, Knight, Chancellor of the Duchy of Lancaster, claiming that William Fleming and John Rusbridger had broken down pilings and banks at his tucking mill.

An exchange of letters on the matter continued through to 1579, when it was alleged that Andrew Foster of Baddesley and Thomas Antrum, miller, had 'with divers and sondrie lewde and desperate persons ... at a certen place called meade Myll pilinges over against Muckson and Baldham entered and with certen stakes .... erected a pilinge over athwart the mayne Channel of the said Ryver and thereby stopped turned and diverted the said Mayne River of Terste out of his aunciente and common Course into the groundes of the said Foster to serve his owne mylls being erected and buylte upon a little Creke or gutte yssuing out of the said Ryver'.

As Andrew Foster was the son of that Abbey Steward who had acquired so much of the monastic property, including the mills, after the dissolution of Romsey Abbey, it seems reasonable to suppose that he owned Mead Mill, on its own stream; equally that Dowse held Sadler's Mill on the main river. The place-name 'Muckson' has not been identified, but 'Baldham' is shown on the Tithe Award Map of 1845 as a meadow near Greatbridge Mill. It is quite close to the point where Mead Mill Stream branches off. A barrier erected across the main river at that point would restrict the flow to Sadler's Mill and encourage more water to flow down to Mead Mill. This increases confidence that the identification of these two mills is correct.

Even in comparatively early times, therefore, water-power was a critical issue, probably because then the inefficiency of water-wheels made them greedy for the strongest possible flow of water. Later problems undoubtedly multiplied because the mills developed in scope and number. By the 18th and 19th centuries there simply was not sufficient water to power all the wheels, as many as four on one site. Some form of shift-working had to be agreed, and beyond that there was cheating. Employees of various mill-owners were clearly expected to undertake subversive activities, giving advantages to their mill.

'The first recorded disturbance that interrupted the former tranquil period was about the year 1776, when the proprietors of new mills came above their own bounds up the River Test & cut away all the rushes flags up to the mouth of the Town and Abbey Mills Stream at the point of separation which had never been done before and also pulled up many stakes called Dowle Stakes being part of the boundaries of the Town Mill Stream; on which prosecution being threatened they desisted till the year 1791 when the same thing was repeated. The offenders were then each of them served with legal notice to desist in future and it has not been repeated until last year 1806.' Thus ran one of the statements given in 1807, when a case was brought against John and Charles May of the Town Mills.

Although the River Test is capable of producing a great deal of power, this was not sufficient for all the water-wheels vying for it. It is not surprising that the serious water supply problems experienced by mill-owners in the late 1700s extended over several decades. Matters came to a head in 1807. Owners working the mills on the main braids of the Test below Greatbridge joined forces. They took legal action against John and Charles May, whose family had worked one or both of the two town centre mills (Town Mill and Abbey Mill) for about a hundred years. The dispute centred upon the amount of water diverted from the Test into the Fishlake to feed the Mays' mills.

A statement written in defence of the Mays implies that there had been no water supply problem to any of the mills up to about 1750, but that during the following ten years all the mills based on the Test had been fitted with additional or more powerful wheels. Collectively, these required some six times the water supply needed prior to conversion. In the case of Burnt Mill and the adjacent Mead Mill, a water shortage appeared immediately the new wheels were put into service. An agreement was reached whereby they would work alternate shifts, 12 hours on and 12 hours off.

All the men working mills on the Test were facing similar difficulties and were desperate to increase the supply to their particular mill. There were a number of ways in which a mill-owner could increase his water supply. He could cut weeds, on the river bed and banks, which impeded the flow upstream of his mill. He could dredge the bottom of the river, reshape the banks and put obstructions in the water to encourage or divert the flow to his benefit. However, given the delicate balance relative to the flow of water to each mill, an improvement in supply to one mill could only be achieved at the expense of another mill, the owner of which would then retaliate by dredging still deeper, etc.

The 1807 Legal Case
Human nature being what it is, such activities and retaliations did take place, and disputes between mill-owners on the river were rife. The result of all their efforts had been to reduce the flow of water down the Fishlake. By the time legal action was taken against the Mays in 1807 the potential for diverting one third of the Test's water along the Fishlake had been reduced in reality to one tenth, and the Mays were not able to work their mills properly.

Nevertheless, after years of squabbling, other mill-owners got together and decided that all their problems were due to the May brothers. The legal case brought against the Mays rested largely on remedial work they had carried out some twenty years earlier. This work, on the river at the junction of the Fishlake, was intended to restore the flow into the Fishlake to its original amount. In the extensive statement made in defence of the Mays, their surprised hurt that such an action should be brought against them is very apparent. They are presented as a couple of nice old chaps 'between 60 and 70 years of age and their memories but little impaired' whose family had for several generations worked the 'Ancient' mills (which, interestingly, they claimed to date back beyond the Domesday book) and who had done their best to avoid any kind of trouble with neighbouring mill-owners. They made the point that their requirement for water had diminished in recent years, due to loss of trade, whereas the requirements of the 'new' mill-owners had increased so enormously that, even if half the water from the Fishlake was put back into the Test, their needs would still not be met.

The objective in bringing an apparently flimsy case against the Mays seems uncertain, since winning would not really have solved the other millers' problems. It is implied in the statement of defence for the Mays that the underlying purpose was to shut down the inner town mills so that the other millers could benefit from the trade that this would release. This suggestion seems entirely compatible with the fact that the investment behind the vastly increased water requirement of the new mills on the river must have required a proportionate increase in trade; and this may not have been forthcoming. In any event, their case did not succeed, since the Mays' mills were still working some 150 years later.

The detailed statements of the 1807 case illuminate the prevailing conditions, problems and rivalries that dominated milling at Romsey. At a pivotal time in the story of milling in the town, the dispute has left behind a wealth of information. It also reflects a continuity of problems, for similar disputes continued into the 20th century.

20th Century Disputes

In the case of Vickers of Greatbridge v Williams of Rivermead, in the early 1900s, a protracted lawsuit placed great emphasis on the distance between wooden stakes set to control water flow, and whether they had been set with the bark on them or not, any bark having been worn away.

Photography played a part in another early 20th-century dispute. In a series of 1911 photographs, a river keeper, simply and rather dismissively referred to as 'Maw', was detailed to stand at various points in the river to demonstrate depths. Sometimes he was almost up to his waist, at other times barely above ankle depth; in one photograph he holds a seemingly significant piece of string. All the photographs are annotated with references to various points A, B, C, etc. In all of them the afflicted Maw gazes sorrowfully and resignedly into the distance. The only concession made to his well-being was a pair of waist-high waders, but otherwise he was very much the lackey.

As the 20th century proceeded, and the mills gradually ceased to work, disputes took a fresh turn. Today's issues centre on fishing rights and access to the riverside.

Plate 6
Maw, the river-keeper, obligingly stands in the water at May's Island
to demonstrate the depth of water at this point
1911

Plate 7
A Water Colour of the Paper Mill at Rivermead
by Fanny Buckell

*LTVAS copy taken from the original in the early 1970s
by arrangement with Romsey Borough Council*

WATER-WHEELS & WATER-POWER

When water-mill technology was in its infancy, the first mill-builders would have been restricted to the most obvious sites, where the essential falls in water levels could be easily achieved, and water-power harnessed by comparatively simple methods. It was only with the development of a range of water-wheels, and gradually increasing sophistication in the machinery, that other sites could be developed to meet growing demands for power. Even so, it was not possible to create mill sites in unfavourable locations.

Good sites for water-mills were thus rare: once a site had been developed, with all the necessary civil engineering works to create the requisite difference in levels, it tended to continue in use. Buildings might be rebuilt, machinery replaced and the power harnessed for different industrial purposes, but the site, with its water supply and its drop in levels, was likely to survive and to serve the community as a source of power for centuries.

Little or nothing is known about the early water-wheels, just before the time of the Domesday Book of 1086: nor is any evidence forthcoming for some considerable time thereafter. Water-wheels, particularly wooden ones, had a life-span of about twenty years. When the time came for them to be replaced, the opportunity would have been taken to incorporate the latest improvements, and all memories of the older wheel would be lost.

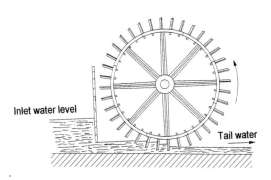

Figure 7: Undershot Wheel

As time passed, water-wheels were designed to suit specific types of location and differing falls in levels. These varied greatly throughout the country. Figures 7, 8, 9 and 10 illustrate the four main types of water-wheel used as technology developed. Of these four types the Undershot Wheel was the simplest, and was usually associated with low falls.

Breast wheels required much more constructional work in the way of weirs, in order to raise the head water to a higher level; the breast itself had to be cut accurately to shape. It is generally believed that they came into use rather later than the Undershot wheel, but precise dates are not known for either. 'Braste Mylnes' are described in Fitzherbert's *The Boke of Surveying*, published in 1539, but were probably well known some time before then.

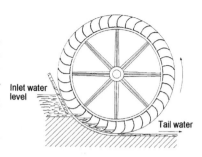

Figure 8: Low Breast Wheel

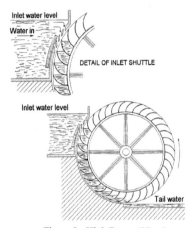

Figure 9: High Breast Wheel

High-Breast Wheels worked on a similar principle, but were better suited to higher falls. They came widely into use in the early years of the 19th century to meet the demands for power to drive the new textile mills and other industries. Their performance was greatly improved by meticulous attention to detail, including sophisticated arrangements for admitting water to the buckets in the most efficient way. They benefited from iron construction, and probably represented the pinnacle of water-wheel development.

Overshot wheels required a fall of water greater than their own diameter and were chosen for sites with high falls. They were simple and efficient, but, unless the site was particularly favourable, much civil engineering work was needed. Little is known of their early history, especially the time they came into use in England. One milepost, often quoted, is an illustration in the Luttrell Psalter printed around 1338.

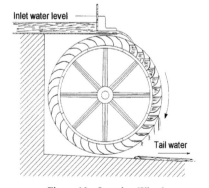

Figure 10: Overshot Wheel

64

Most of the Romsey mills, as known in later years, had a fall of about five feet (1.5 metres) - rather less at Burnt Mill and Mead Mill, rather more at Town Mill and significantly more at the Abbey Mill. It was the height of the fall that determined the choice of water-wheel, and the average of five feet at most of Romsey mills meant that the Low-Breast Wheel would be preferred. The lower arc of these wheels was enclosed in a 'breast', usually of dressed stone, which followed the curvature of the wheel closely. This prevented the water from escaping until it had done its work on the wheel, and in this way the power of the water was used more effectively.

It is possible to relate what is known of Romsey's water-wheels to the background just established. Early evidence comes from the Burnt Mill and Mead Mill complex. In the early 18th century, Burnt Mill had been described as a grist-mill with one small water-wheel. By 1753 this had been upgraded to 'a large water-wheel of three times the power', and some time later two water-wheels were installed 'capable of being divided into two complete corn-mills'. But even in 1807 these could only be worked together when there was plenty of water. Meanwhile, its neighbour, Mead Mill, had been upgraded from 'One Tucking Mill Wheel' to 'One large wheel for a paper-mill'. Mead Mill and Burnt Mill both drew their water from the same source, the Mead Mill Stream: as indicated before, water shortage made it impossible to work both mills at the same time, and the shift system was devised. Out of three water-wheels on this site, there were occasions when it was only possible to work one.

Nearby Test Mill had three water-wheels for 'a large paper manufactory' as far back as 1768. By 1818 the main mill had four water-wheels, and the little '12 perch' mill just upstream, which by this time had been taken over by the paper-mill, had a water-wheel of its own. So there were five water-wheels on this site. When the mill was demolished, in 1997, just one water-wheel remained. It was of iron construction, 10 feet (3 metres) in diameter and of the low-breast type. Nothing is known of the others.

Rivermead Mill had the benefit of water from both the Mead Mill Stream and the Test Mill Stream. Fortunately, the report of a survey made in 1878 still survives. It lists a total of four water-wheels at Rivermead. In one building there were two water-wheels, one large and one small, whilst a narrow water-wheel was in another building. A new iron breast-shot wheel of 50 horse-power was in a newly-built timber and slate building. Even in the late 19th century a 50 horse-power wheel would have been rather special.

On the south-western edge of town, Sadler's Mill in 1887 had a 'Nearly-New Breast-Shot Water-wheel by Munden and Armfield, 13 feet diameter' and an 'Iron Frame Undershot wheel 11 feet diameter' (4 metres and 3.4 metres respectively). Here the fall of the water was 5 feet 6 inches (1.7 metres), so the breast-shot wheel was probably the better of the two. Munden and Armfield were millwrights and engineers in Ringwood. They supplied much of the mill equipment in the area.

Fox Mill, on the Tadburn tributary, is interesting because of its struggles for water. Notionally, it used the water from the Tadburn Stream, but right from the outset, as already mentioned, it had been necessary to supplement this with waste water from the canal. Even then it could only realise 4 horse-power. After the canal closed, arrangements were made to take more water from its surviving section, and the output at the mill went up to 6 horse-power. Later, by transferring water from the River Test into the old canal - and then into the Tadburn upstream of Fox Mill - the output was increased to 8 horse-power. But, inevitably, this arrangement met with protests from Mr Zillwood, who then worked the Abbey Mill. He saw any diversion of water from the Test into the old canal as a threat to his own mill, and so he nailed the hatch shut. The usual polemics followed.

In 1811, when Fox Mill was only about eleven years old, William Soffe, the miller at the time, appealed to the Pavement Commissioners about his rates assessment. He apparently paid £20 per annum but his mill could not work more than 6 hours in 24 during the summer. On the other hand, according to Mr Soffe, one of the mills called Abbey Mill (either Abbey Mill or Rivermead Mill) could work night and day and yet was charged only £35. Soffe further explained that he was unable to make up his average in the winter because of an excess of water. This surprising statement suggests that the 'excess' was water that could not escape quickly enough downstream from the water-wheel: so it would back up and effectively choke the wheel. This was a long recognised problem. Back in 1539, when Fitzherbert was writing his *Boke of Surveying*, he advised that the water should flow 'when it is past the mylne, with a sufficient fall of the water that the mylne stand not in back water, to return the ryver ageyn'.

Perhaps the most interesting details relate to the two urban mills powered by the Fishlake Stream. When the Town Mill was advertised for sale in 1881, it had two breast-shot water-wheels, one of 12 horse-power, the other 10 horse-power. A later document of 1882 reveals that a new iron water-wheel was installed by the *Test Valley Ironworks*, a local firm of millwrights and iron-founders. The wheel was 15 feet 6 inches (4.7 metres) in diameter and 6 feet (1.8 metres) wide; it cost £148 10s 0d. Thus a water-wheel nearly two storeys high was generating little more than 12 horse-power. By comparison, a small family saloon car has about 60 horse-power. Clearly, it was difficult, and expensive, to harness the power of water: and the rewards, by present day standards, were small. But, when water-wheels were the only sources of power available, almost any effort was worthwhile.

Not only was the power of water difficult and expensive to realise, but the supply of water may have been uncertain. 'The water supply being generally abundant' was the phrase used when Town Mill was offered for sale in 1881. Only three years earlier, however, a report prepared for the then tenant in support of his application for a rent reduction, claimed that 'the water supply is usually very scanty at the latter part of the summer when the grist and flour trades are most brisk'.

The final mill to be considered is the Abbey Mill, interesting because it incorporated examples of the two remaining types of water-wheel. There had been a corn-mill on this site for many years, but some time between 1813 and 1822 a flax-mill had been added close by. In 1832 the corn-mill had an overshot wheel and the flax-mill had a 'New Cast Iron Overshot Bucket Wheel 16 feet diameter and 10 feet wide' (4.9 metres and 3 metres respectively). The fall here was about 4.4 metres. Remembering that the diameter of an overshot wheel must be less than the fall, the corn-mill may, in 1832, have had an overshot wheel about 12 feet (3.65 metres) in diameter. But the water-wheel at the flax-mill was claimed to be 16 feet (4.9 metres) in diameter. This would appear to have been larger than the fall, which is still only 4.4 metres, and seems to make a nonsense of the advertisement. At that time, in the early part of the 19th century, the high-breast water-wheel would have been the number one choice, whenever possible.

Water-wheels replaced by Turbines
Just a few years later, though, a more efficient alternative to the cumbersome water-wheel was introduced. It was called a 'turbine'. The water turbine was invented in France by Benoit Fourneyron in 1827. It is a hydrodynamic machine, made completely of metal. Within it are sets of curved metal blades. Water flows continuously over these blades, which are cleverly designed to utilise the power of the water to best advantage, and so produce the required rotary motion. Compared with a water-wheel, the turbine turns

more quickly, and it is very much smaller. This means it is also lighter, cheaper and easier to install.

Yet, despite all these advantages, some time elapsed before water turbines became popular in England. By the end of the 19th century, however, some of the mills in Romsey had fitted them. Town Mill had made the switch by 1892. This was the year that Mr Meddings wrote to his insurance company to advise them that his mill was driven by turbines and that these 'are under water and so cannot be damaged by fire'. He was right; but because they were under water they were also out of sight, and never achieved anything of the picturesque image associated with water-wheels. This is unfortunate, because a turbine's internal working parts have an elegant simplicity and a beauty of form that surpasses anything a water-wheel could offer.

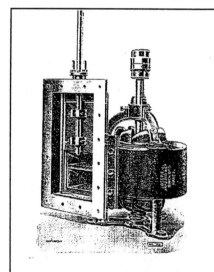

Figure 11: A 'British Empire' Turbine
by kind permission of Biwater Industries Ltd

An article in *The Miller* magazine in 1895 reveals that the two turbines at Town Mill were 'British Empire' turbines made by J.J.Armfield and Company of Ringwood: their 'British Empire' turbines were widely used and very successful. The two at Town Mill continued to provide power for over sixty years, and were only replaced by electric motors in the last few years before the mill closed.

Abbey Mill had installed a 'Little Giant' turbine by 1895. This was another popular model of American design. Rivermead Mill gradually fitted more and more until eventually it had four turbines to drive the leatherboard factory. At least two of these were still in use in 1968 when the mill closed.

In later years several more turbines were installed in different locations for a variety of purposes, described towards the end of the next chapter, under the sub-heading 'Other Uses for Water-power'.

ROMSEY'S WATER-WHEELS: Their Uses & Processes

1   Corn-milling

At the time of the Domesday Survey, Romsey's mills would have served exclusively for grinding corn, one of the most essential processes for day-to-day living. When prehistoric people had chosen to make cereals an important part of their diet, they had also committed themselves, and their descendants, to the unrelenting, tedious and never-ending labour of grinding the grains in order to produce the much desired flour. Widespread relief from this drudgery was only achieved in this country about a thousand years ago with the introduction of mills to harness water-power. For a long time corn-grinding was the only purpose for mills.

Early Methods of Grinding Corn by Hand

Primitive methods of reducing grains to flour started with pounding in a mortar with a hand-held pestle. The next stage introduced a more efficient rubbing action, by which the grains were ground between a stationary saddle-stone and a smaller rubbing stone that was moved to-and-fro, again by hand. Then, with the development of the rotary quern, the rubbing technique was further refined into a continuous process. The grain was now ground between two circular stone discs, the lower stone again remaining stationary, whilst this time the upper one was rotated above it. Grain was fed into a central hole in the upper stone and was broken up as it worked its way to the rim, where it emerged as flour. These mills were on a domestic scale, producing the daily needs of a household, and they were still driven by hand.

How did the Corn-mill Work?

The water-mill's stones were scaled up to a larger size. The hard work was now done by the water-wheel, but the principle was the same as that of the quern. This situation held good until the water-mill was finally displaced by the roller-mill at the end of the 19th and beginning of the 20th century.

Inside the water-mill, the stones lay flat and needed to be turned around a vertical axis about a hundred times a minute. The water-wheel, however, rotated about a horizontal axis about ten times a minute. So a complex arrangement of gears was required to redirect the drive from the horizontal axis of the water-wheel to the vertical axis of the stones, and to increase the speed of rotation by a factor of ten or thereabouts. This transmission was effected by gearing, and Figure 12 helps to explain how this worked. Starting at the water-wheel the first pair of gears turned the drive from horizontal to vertical, and also contributed the first step in the speeding-up process. The second pair completed the speeding-up, and the stones could rotate at the proper speed.

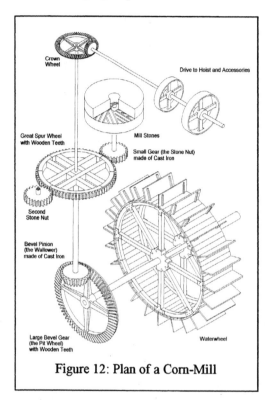

Great Spur Wheel with Wooden Teeth
Crown Wheel
Drive to Hoist and Accessories
Mill Stones
Small Gear (the Stone Nut) made of Cast Iron
Second Stone Nut
Bevel Pinion (the Wallower) made of Cast Iron
Large Bevel Gear (the Pit Wheel) with Wooden Teeth
Waterwheel

Figure 12: Plan of a Corn-Mill

Originally, all the gear-wheels would have been wooden, early examples of precision joinery. Even when cast-iron gears became available it was normal to retain wooden teeth in the larger wheel of each pair. This continued until the mills finally closed, generally within the last hundred years. Eventually, very much less frequently than might be expected, the teeth wore out and had to be replaced; a skilled job for the millwright. When the Abbess leased the Town Mill to John King in 1533, she stipulated that he should 'repair and maintain all manner of repairs pertaining to the same house, viz., in dawbinge, thetchinge, ringinge and cogginge ... at his own proper cost'. The 'cogginge' refers to the renewal of the wooden gear teeth, when required. Centuries later, in 1887, a survey of the same mill observed that one of the gears needed new cogs. That same year the *Test Valley Ironworks*, which at that time worked from premises in The Hundred, sent a quotation for £6 10s 0d for fitting 166 dry hornbeam wood cogs. Hornbeam was a favoured wood for this job, as were also apple and beech.

The Mill-stones
The mill-stones themselves are worth detailed attention. For making flour the preferred stones were French, made from a special type of flint called burr-stone, which was quarried a little way to the east of Paris. As the stone only occurred in small pieces, the mill-stones were built up from small

70

segments fitted closely together, making them easily recognisable. Imports into England had certainly begun by 1587, probably earlier, and the French burr-stones remained the favourites right up to the time when the mills finally closed. All the available inventories of Romsey mills included some. These same inventories also included Peak stones, made from a special sandstone found in the Peak District of Derbyshire. As this stone was available from the quarries in large pieces, a mill-stone could be made from a single piece. Generally, Peak stones were used for grinding barley, oats and other animal foods, keeping the best French stones for flour.

The sketch given in Figure 12 has a pictorial cut-away in the upper stone to reveal the pattern of grooves cut into the upper surface of the lower stone. An identical pattern was cut into the lower surface of the upper stone. These grooves, or furrows, helped to break up the grain during its journey from the centre to the rim of the stone. Equally importantly, they allowed air to accompany the grain, and this helped to keep it cool. The grooves, and the flat areas between them, had to be recut at intervals to maintain an efficient grinding surface. This recutting was a highly skilled job, often done by itinerant craftsmen; it continued into the 20th century. Mr Tommy Fryer, who in his early years prior to 1934 worked for the *Test Valley Ironworks*, recalls travelling around the local mills to dress their stones. Mr John Ormsby, who worked at the Town Mill shortly after the Second World War, and who has recorded his memories, was taught to dress the stones by the mill-foreman. In this mill they evidently did the job themselves, but the skill requirement would have been the same.

Ownership in the Early Days and 'Soke'
Building a mill in the early medieval period required a heavy capital investment, which only a substantial landowner could make. Having laid out good money for this purpose the landowner then attempted to increase his chances of receiving an adequate return by a system known as 'Soke'. This meant that tenants of a particular lord were obliged to take their corn to his mill for grinding, and to no other mill. Even hand-mills, for use in the privacy of the tenants' own homes, were forbidden. No doubt the lords would claim such a scheme was necessary to justify their outlay; doubtless the tenants took a rather different view. Nonetheless, it does appear that grudging acceptance was, in general, preferable to the drudgery of grinding the meal by hand; and there was certainly no other option for a farmer with a goodly amount of grain for processing. Penalties could be exacted for violations of the Soke rules.

In the case of Romsey the medieval landlord was the Abbess, as lord of the manors of Romsey Infra and Romsey Extra. When tenants of Lee and Woobury, in the southern part of Romsey Extra, dared to take their corn to the nearby mill in Skidmore, they were warned that they would be fined, if the offence was repeated.

'Soke' as a scheme appears to have been established before the arrival of the Normans. It continued into the post-medieval period, though freemen were winning exemption from the obligations of Soke as early as the end of the 13th century. It seems likely that the system was almost, but not quite, finished by the early 16th century. By that time most men had gained their freedom, and ownership of mills was passing from the lords into the hands of merchants and capitalists. This was particularly true where mills had been held by monastic institutions dissolved by Henry VIII.

The Miller's Thumb

Until the 18th century the miller was paid in kind: even the apprentice had his own small proportion. Customers brought their corn to the mill; the miller ground it and then took a fraction of the flour for himself. He was then allowed to sell this flour to raise money for his own needs. The miller's share was prescribed, and may have once related to the feudal status of the customer. Thus a freeman may have paid just one-sixteenth part, perhaps in recognition of his option to use a competitor's mill, perhaps because he brought a larger quantity of grain. The bondsman, on the other hand, may have been obliged to contribute one-twelfth of his flour in payment: it is easy to appreciate his growing resentment. Since the stones were supposed to be cleaned down after each customer's load, the scale of charges in later years probably related more directly to the amount of grain brought to the mill, again to the detriment of the small producer.

Popular opinion implied that the miller may have taken rather more than his fair share by continually inserting his thumb inside the top of the measuring bin to present a false amount, and thus gradually winning more flour for himself. This suspected habit may have inspired Chaucer's description of his miller:

> His was a master hand at stealing grain,
> He felt it with his thumb and thus he knew
> Its quality and took three times his due -
> A thumb of Gold, by God, to gauge an oat!

By the 18th century the miller's relationship with his customers had changed. Now he began to buy corn direct from farmers on his own account. He ground it in his mill, and then sold the flour to the public. In local trade directories millers began to describe themselves as 'mealmen'. In 1784, for example, Benjamin Dawkins was mealman at Sadler's Mill and William Card was miller and mealman at Burnt Mill. As well as indicating their new role as dealers in flour, perhaps millers also saw the new title as a means of shaking off the unsavoury reputation inherited from their forebears.

Changes in Corn-Milling in the 18th Century

In 18th-century Romsey it seems that both technical improvement and expansion in corn-grinding capacity led to an increased demand for power, and hence for a greater strength of water flow to each mill. Problems culminated in the next century with the 1807 dispute about water supplies.

During the 18th century, Burnt Mill was upgraded from a grist-mill with one water-wheel to a corn-mill powered by two water-wheels. Burnt Mill was also equipped with flour-dressing machinery that allowed for finer separation of the flour, and the change of description from 'grist-mill' to 'corn-mill' may have striven to reflect this improved product. Sadler's Mill received similar improvements. Town Mill retained its two water-wheels for grinding flour, added flour-dressing machinery, stopped grinding malt and removed the water-wheel that had previously driven the malt-mill. Only Abbey Mill, which had already been equipped with flour-dressing machinery at the beginning of the century, remained unchanged. There must have been a very large increase in trade to justify, or to require, investment in new plant on such a scale. Indeed, there seems to have been sufficient increase in demand to warrant the construction of an entirely new mill. This was Fox Mill, established in 1799.

The expansion just related took place at a time when, nationally, the population was increasing, and when agricultural methods and practices were changing rapidly. The enclosure movement was well under way. Greater priority was being given to growing cereals, and new land was being ploughed for this purpose. A similar pattern is indicated for the Romsey area. Local millers were eager to profit from the expansion, and each was determined that the available water-power should work to his advantage.

By 1807, when the invaluable document concerning the state of Romsey mills was written, all the corn-mills in Romsey had been equipped with flour-dressing machinery. Abbey Mill merited special attention in respect of 'the Grandfather of the present Mays, who first set up the new bolting machinery in this part of the country about the year 1708, ...'. The implication was that the setting up of such machinery had been a pioneering step at the beginning of the 18th century. The purpose of the bolter, or flour-dressing machine, was to separate the bran from the flour. In use, the meal passed along a sleeve of woven cloth drawn over a wooden frame. The sleeve had a gentle inclination and was rotated by an auxiliary drive from the main machinery. As it turned, the flour passed through the weave of the cloth, whilst the bran and other coarse particles continued to the far end, where they were collected separately and sold for animal food. The flour that was separated out was finer and whiter, and was much preferred. This explains why most mills eventually had either a bolter or a later variant, called a 'wire-machine', which appeared after woven wire gauzes became available.

All these dressing-machines needed power to drive them, and they also generated more work for the hoist. Initially, the hoist was used simply to raise the corn from the delivery cart to a high point in the mill - the bin loft or bin floor. The high projecting gable, or luccam, which was a feature of many corn-mills, was associated with the hoist. Carts could pull up below it and the hoist had a clear lift straight up to the bin loft. From the bin loft the grain would flow downwards by gravity, through the grinding mill proper, and finally arrive as flour on the ground floor. From there it could be despatched.

With the introduction of flour-dressing machines the basic flour arriving on the ground floor had to be returned to a higher level, so that it could make a second descent through the screens of the bolter or wire machine. The hoist consumed power. In 1807 it was reported that the old water-wheel at Burnt Mill '... was not capable of drawing dressing tackle', but that afterwards the '... new large wheel of three times the power', which replaced the old wheel in 1753, was installed expressly 'to grind, work dressing and hoisting tackle at the same time ....'. William Card was the miller.

In the 19th century demands for power continued to rise with the introduction of machines to clean the grain before grinding. For example, Town Mill by 1871 had installed a smut machine; Greatbridge Mill had a smut machine in 1880; and by 1901 Abbey Mill had a 'Victor Smut and Separator Machine'. Smut is a black fungus that attacks wheat, and the smut machine was designed to remove it by scouring the grains. The separators were provided to remove soil, small stones, loose straw and chaff. Both devices suggest an increasing concern with cleanliness and quality. Before the introduction of these machines, dust and dirt were removed from the grain in a sieve called a 'temse', which was shaken to-and-fro by hand.

The mechanical cleaning-machines not only required power for themselves, but they also introduced additional hoisting operations. In some cases, elaborate systems of elevators and conveyors were installed to move the material from one processing machine to the next. In 1887 Mr Minchington, a Romsey millwright, sent a quotation to Mr Bate of Town Mill for 'One new wheat elevator complete fitted to smut machine. Also to enclose smut machine in wood frame and find all necessary shafting, pulleys, belts, etc. to drive same. Also new Iron Worm conveyor 17ft long to convey wheat from elevator to grading bins. All for £26 5s 0d'. Worm conveyors were like giant screws, which, by rotation, moved the grain or meal along a trough. Elevators had metal scoops fitted onto an endless leather belt. They scooped up the grain or meal from a bin at the bottom and emptied it into another on a higher floor. Quite a number were included in the inventory of Abbey Mill in 1900. With the machines themselves, and the drives to them, the hoists, elevators and conveyors, and the drives to them also, the mill was becoming a complicated affair. And, with every addition, it needed more and more power. Although technology improved, the demands for increased power stretched the source of that power to the limit.

Roller-Mills and the Beginning of the End
Towards the end of the 19th century the small country mills were exposed to pressures that initially led to changes, later to closure. Following the repeal of the Corn Laws in 1846, the duty on imported corn was reduced. By 1869 it had been reduced to zero. Most histories suggest that the repeal of the Corn Laws was a contributory factor in the decline of the country mill. But 1869 was also the year when the Trans-America Railway was completed. It thus became possible to transport grain easily and cheaply from the Prairies to the American East Coast ports, and from there to Europe. Technical developments, ideally suited to the processing and distribution of this vast new supply of grain, were beginning to inspire new machines. Once these came into general use the small mills were on borrowed time. Indeed, it now seems remarkable that they managed to struggle on for so long.

On the mechanical front the important change was the introduction of the roller-mill. This innovation had been developed on the Continent before

1840, and by about 1870 its advantages had become apparent in this country. Roller-mills produced white flour, increasingly in demand from the public. Moreover, they were well suited to grind the harder wheats arriving from America, and they could be incorporated into large plants. Accordingly, these new-style mills were constructed on a vast scale. The steam-engine, increasingly sophisticated, was now able to meet the correspondingly vast appetites for power, and the steam railways were available to carry the products to any place in the land. The miller's market was no longer restricted to the immediate surrounding area. He was not limited to grinding locally grown corn for consumption by local people. Above all, it was no longer necessary to build mills alongside rivers to find sources of power. The new steam mills could be built anywhere: and there was nowhere better than alongside the quays where the American imports were arriving, and where the ships could discharge grain directly into the mill.

Roller-mills worked on an entirely different principle from the grindstones of the country mill. They brought the first fundamental change in the method and tradition of producing flour, which had remained unchanged for several thousands of years. The new technique involved the crushing of the grains between rollers, like a mangle, as opposed to the grinding of grain between mill-stones, whether powered by hand, water or wind. The roller-mills worked very much faster than the old traditional grind-stones, and they reduced the grain to flour in several stages. Complicated sieving arrangements were incorporated between the stages, and elaborate systems of elevators and conveyors transported the various grades from one machine to the next. Roller-mills were essentially factories, and flour production changed from a small craft workshop to an industrial enterprise.

The Country Mill Fights On
The country mills did respond to this challenge. Some installed roller plant to produce the fine white flour demanded by the public. With only limited power available, however, the installations were much smaller than those in the new industrial mills springing up near the sea-ports. Sadler's Mill was offered for sale in 1887 with '2 pairs of Rollers with all necessary machinery and appliances'. In 1895 Town Mill was listed in Kelly's Directory as 'Town Roller-mills'; an insurance policy of 1918 included three sets of rollers. Abbey Mill responded likewise: in 1900, the magazine *The Miller* reported on 'Mr LeQuesne who came over from Guernsey to run the Abbey Mills at Romsey, into which he had put a small roller plant ....'. Mr LeQuesne had taken the lease on the mill from the Sisters of La Sagesse in

1896. In 1901, an inventory of the mill included 'two Armfield Double Roller-mills' and one 'Double Victoria dustless Purifier'. The latter was for sifting the meal between stages of the rolling process.

By using roller-machines the local mills could possibly match the whiteness of flour demanded by their customers, and so compete, for a while, with the steam-mills. But a letterhead of Mr W.E. Holloway, the miller at Sadler's Mill in 1913, offers 'Grinding and Crushing of every description at shortest notice', giving a clue to another strategy for survival - the preparation of animal food. He was not alone.

Diversifying into animal food meant that mill machinery lists gradually became more varied. Some idea of early changes may be gleaned from the story of Town Mill. An 1871 inventory records that there were four pairs of French stones (for flour), of which two pairs were badly worn. By 1888, when George Barton Budd leased the same mill, there were just two pairs of French Stones: perhaps replacement of the worn pairs had not been worthwhile at a time when roller plant was beginning to take over. Moreover, by that year an oat-and-bean crusher had been acquired, and the mill had two pairs of Peak stones, most probably for grinding oats or barley. The 1918 insurance policy that mentioned the three sets of rollers also itemised 'Two pairs of stones (oats being ground for cattle)'.

Mr John Ormsby, who began work at the Town Mill around 1946, and continued as the manager there until it closed in 1968, remembers that the mill was a compound feed mill and by then produced no flour. Whilst learning the trade he worked on the mixers, on a seed-cleaning plant, on a maize-cutter and on grinders for barley, wheat, meal, etc., producing chicken feed and making up compound feeds. The grains were mainly bought from local farmers within a radius of 20 or 30 miles, though some supplies were imported and used to come in from Southampton. Mr Tommy Fryer, who drove lorries for the Town Mill just after the Second World War, went round delivering to farms within the area of Hampshire and Wiltshire, but had to travel to Bristol, London and Avonmouth to pick up supplies. The suggestion is that the local mill could still enjoy some advantages by serving the local farming community.

Meanwhile, Abbey Mill was described in an 1895 advertisement in *The Miller* magazine as 'doing a good country flour, offal, corn and feed grinding trade'. An inventory of 1901 included a Bentalls Oat-and-Bean Crusher and one meal mixer amongst its assets.

Despite these valiant efforts all Romsey's corn-mills closed eventually, although in most cases the precise year of closure is not known. The last reference found for Greatbridge Mill is in Kelly's Directory for 1898, when George Longland Aylward was the miller, but how much longer it operated is unknown.

Fox Mill burned down in 1890. It was rebuilt but never worked as a corn-mill again; its entire working life had lasted only 91 years. Burnt Mill kept going with Mr William Ellis as the miller until at least 1915, when he is listed in Kelly's Directory. His billhead describes the business as 'Miller, Ovum, Linseed and Cotton Cake, Corn, Hay, Straw, Chaff, Offals and Meal Merchant - Vienna and other Flour, Whole Meal etc.', a telling statement of how the miller's work had changed. The mill changed hands some time later, and again in 1925. It is thought that milling stopped around that time.

Fire destroyed Abbey Mill in 1925, and the site was redeveloped as an extension for the Convent of the Sisters of La Sagesse. Sadler's Mill corn-mill appears to have kept going until 1931, this date being the last mention found so far in the trade directories. Perhaps fittingly, Town Mill did best of all. It continued to produce animal foods until it finally closed in 1968. It is unfortunate that the name given to the shopping precinct on its site makes no acknowledgement of the Town Mill, which, for perhaps 900 years, had ground corn and grain to feed the people and the animals of Romsey.

2   Fulling

Fulling was a finishing process for woollen cloth. The object was to clean the cloth of grease and oil after weaving, and then to pound it so that the fibres matted together. In the process the cloth would shrink and the resulting cloth resembled a blanket. Woollen cloths made from short woollen fibres were cleaned (scoured) and pounded. Worsteds, made from longer woollen fibres, were only scoured.

Originally the cloth was fulled in a fulling pit, a trough of water to which was added fuller's earth (a kind of clay) or some other detergent, such as urine or wood ash. Workers would 'walk', or tread, the cloth in the fulling pit; the surname 'Walker' most probably derives from this work. By the end of the 12th century the process was becoming mechanised with the introduction of fulling stocks, or hammers, driven by a water-wheel. The work, which had been largely town-based, migrated to the best sources of water-power. Fulling-mills, powered by water-wheels, were built to meet this need; they were sometimes called tucking mills.

After corn-grinding, fulling was one of the first processes to be mechanised. The earliest records of English fulling-mills date from 1185 and relate to Newsham in Yorkshire, and to Burton, near Temple Guiting, in the Cotswolds. This last mill was owned by the Knights Templar, who probably introduced the concept from the Continent. Romsey was not too far behind; references to a fulling-mill during the reign of Edward I (1272-1307) have already been mentioned. The town was well-placed for this work. Quite apart from the available water power, it was conveniently situated at the heart of a triangle based on the medieval cloth centres of Southampton, Winchester and Salisbury.. The proximity of Southampton, which traded in fuller's earth, was particularly relevant, whilst Romsey Abbey had links with the Salisbury area through landholdings in Wiltshire.

Figure 13: Fulling Stocks

Fulling Stocks resembled hammers with their shafts upright. The shafts were pivoted at their upper ends so that they could swing like pendula, as shown in Figure 13. The hammers were raised by tappets on a rotating shaft, driven by the water-wheel to a height of approximately 2 feet 8 inches (80 centimetres). They were then released so that they could swing down by gravity to strike the cloth, which was bundled up in the trough with the water and detergent. Typically, each hammer would make about 39 strokes per minute. Two hammers worked in each trough.

Fulling a piece of cloth 30 yards long could take all day. Occasionally, the cloth was removed to measure the shrinkage, and fulling continued until it had shrunk by the required amount. The cloth was then washed to remove the detergent and stretched on tenter-frames. These drying and stretching frames were erected in nearby fields or orchards. The cloth was reshaped and resized on closely-placed hooks around the tenter-frame, giving rise to the phrase 'being on tenterhooks'. The tenter-frames were sometimes called 'racks', and two fields bearing the name 'Rack Close' have been identified in Romsey. One of these fields was just north of Mill Lane.

Growth of the Manufacture of Woollen Cloth in the 14th Century

Through the 11th and 12th centuries English wool was widely regarded; at that time much of it was exported as raw wool or fleeces. Abbeys, with their Continental connections, were well-placed to carry on this trade. Romsey Abbey was in a particularly good position to participate, since it owned the Wiltshire sheep-rearing lands of Edington and Imber, granted by King Edgar in 968AD. The effect on the town is unknown, but it may have benefited.

By the 13th century there was a shift towards making finished cloth in England, a movement that was further encouraged by Edward III who, in the 1330s, invited Flemish weavers, dyers and fullers to come and work in this country. The demand for fulling-mills increased accordingly. When, in 1428, William Berrell rented from the Abbess a site for a fulling-mill by Chavy Water, he was probably responding to an expansion in the manufacture of cloth around that time.

It was a useful coincidence that, throughout this period, Romsey was the first stage for Southampton traders on their inland routes to more distant places such as Salisbury, Exeter, Bristol, Oxford, Gloucester and Leicester. Moreover, in the 15th century, hauliers were carrying raw cloth through the gates of Southampton to Romsey for fulling. The cloth was often returned to Southampton for shipping. In 1443 the Southampton Brokage Books record that five cartloads of cloth went to Romsey, and they were evidently expected to return through Southampton, as no custom was charged.

The Chavy Water undertaking, which may not have come to fruition, was not the earliest reference to a Romsey fulling-mill. The mill on the stream off the upper Holbrook in the time of Edward I has already been mentioned. Two other mills may date back some time before any mention of them is found in documentary records. Mead Mill, with its fulling stocks, was clearly well-established by the time it was granted to Thomas Thoroughgood and John Foster in 1545; the fulling-mill at Spursholt (Sadler's) Mill, referred to in a dispute over water in 1573, had also probably existed for some while.

A hint of the importance and long existence of the fulling-mills is given in a 16th-century letter pursuing the dispute about water supplies. Written in

1579 it claims that: 'for as long as the memory of man there have been divers and sondrie grist mylls and fullinge mylls serving not onlie the Towne of Romsey but the whole of the countrie near and adjoining the town'.

Manufacture of Shalloons in the 18th and 19th Centuries

After the Tudor period there is a considerable gap before the next reference to cloth-fulling appears. It concerns an unspecified mill on Test Mill Stream, where there was, in 1708, 'one small water-wheel used for Tucking and used in the manufacture of Shalloons'. Dr Johnson, in his great 18th-century dictionary, defined Shalloon as 'a slight woollen stuff'; it appears to have been used mainly for coat-linings and for women's dresses.

In 1800 the Land Tax assessments for Cherville Street tything assessed a small 'Mill and House' at 4s 3d. This was the '12 perch' mill, situated just to the north of Test Mill and fed by the same Test Mill Stream. From 1800 to 1809 it was occupied by Thomas Munday and owned by James Sharp, who was listed in Sadler's Directory for 1784 as a linen draper and shalloon manufacturer. It seems reasonable to assume that the mill was contributing to the manufacture of Shalloons. Quite early on in the 19th century, though, its contribution to the town's long-established cloth trade was a thing of the past; the coal fields of the north had drawn the cloth industry away from the south, and the great days lived on only in memory.

According to that invaluable source, Dr Latham, 'In the memory of some old inhabitants a thousand hands at least were employed in the looms and other occupations in the wool branch'. As the total population for Romsey was probably below 4,000 during the 18th century, allowance must be made for exaggeration. People were remembering the principal product of their day, a cloth called 'Broad Rash'. Although 'rash' was well-regarded as a silk or cloth fabric with a smooth finish, the broad rash made in Romsey seems to have been of inferior quality. Dr Latham described it as 'a coarse cloth formerly in much use called Broad Rash. ...... The Gowns worn by the Brothers of St Cross [Winchester] are of Broad Rash'. Perhaps the quality of the cloth produced in Romsey gradually deteriorated.

James Sharp's little mill was the last echo of fulling-mills in Romsey. Fulling-mills continued in use in some areas, especially Yorkshire, until the mid-1900s, but in many cases the hammer-type fulling stocks were replaced by a roller-type machine invented by John Dyer of Trowbridge in 1833.

81

Fulling-mills for curing leather

It appears that fulling stocks were also used for curing sheepskins. The sheepskin was split and the inner layer (flesh side) was cured by impregnating it with cod liver oil to produce chamois leather. The fulling stocks were used to impress the oil by repeated blows of the hammers. The leather so produced was often bleached and dyed and used for gloves, and Romsey has been home to several glovemakers.

In 1783 Lord Palmerston sold the oil-and-skin mill adjacent to Sadler's Mill to Elizabeth Baker, and it is interesting that the sale documents mention lime pits associated with this mill. A preliminary process for removing the wool from the sheepskins involved soaking the skins in lime. So, whilst this small mill may have been used originally for fulling cloth, it appears to have been used for dressing leather well before the end of the 18th century. The mill was supplied with water by a 'little cut', adequate enough for this purpose. This same mill later became a sawmill for a short time. This is a typical example of change of use, whilst retaining the advantage of the water-power available at the site. After the sawmill closed the buildings were finally demolished around 1865.

3   Paper-making

It is thought that the Moors introduced paper-making into Spain around 1150AD. From there it spread into Italy and France, but only later into England. Until the end of the 15th century, when the first English mills started to appear, paper had to be imported from the Continent. Even then diffusion was slow, despite a rapidly increasing demand for books and newspapers, and the growing preference of lawyers and business men to record their transactions on paper. At the same time there was a similar increase in the demand for wrapping papers.

Romsey appears to have been well placed for the manufacture of paper. It had good supplies of clean water as well as established water-power. Also, paper-making demanded pounding techniques similar to those of fulling, in which Romsey had long been expert. This was opportune, since Romsey, in common with other similar market towns in the 18th century, needed a replacement for the failing cloth trade. After a slowish start, paper-making became an important industry in the town for something like 200 years. Indeed, Test Mill continued to make paper into the 1930s, while Rivermead Mill carried on a closely related process, making leatherboard, until it finally closed in 1967.

Around 1675, though, there were only a few paper-mills in England, and the country was still heavily dependent on imports. Then, to counter this unsatisfactory state of affairs, there appears to have been a nation-wide surge in paper-making, and Romsey may have been an early participant in that expansion. Dr Latham reported a 1733 lawsuit against John Hockley, proprietor of 'the Paper-mill which had been erected about 50 years before by his predecessor', suggesting that Mr Hockley's mill had been built around 1683. This is not an unreasonable speculation. There were already five paper-mills in Hampshire by 1685, including the important Up Mill in Southampton, as well as two or more in the Salisbury region. Romsey might well have been another early centre for this new industry. It is even possible that the mill erected on the Rivermead site was built specifically for the purpose of making paper. With potential for extra water-power from the newly-cut Straight Stream, good clean water from a spring and an awareness of paper-making in the region, Rivermead would have provided a welcome and very opportune contribution to the restructuring of the town's economic base.

Making the Paper
Paper-making in those early mills began with the sorting of rags. These were cut into small squares and then soaked in water until they began to ferment. They were then placed in a trough with water, and pounded with hammers. This was where the requirement for water-power arose; the hammers were lifted by cams on the water-wheel shaft, and then released so that they fell by gravity onto the rags in the trough below. The principle was entirely similar to the fulling-mill and it is easy to see why many fulling-mills were switched to paper-making. It was an ideal transfer of production.

Pounding the rags was a slow process. The first stage used hammers faced with pointed iron nails to reduce the rags to pulp, at this stage called 'half-stuff'. This was sufficiently processed for wrapping paper, which could be made directly from the half-stuff pulp. For white paper, however, the pulp needed more pounding, this time with hammers faced with flatter nails to produce 'whole-stuff'. Finally, smooth wooden hammers were used to produce pulp of an even texture. Thus prepared, the stuff was diluted with clean water in a vat and stirred thoroughly to distribute the fibres. The mixture would require frequent stirring whilst paper was being made in order to keep the fibres distributed. Most mills were 'one-vat mills'. Although some had two vats, mills with three or four vats would have been exceptional.

If John Hockley's mill at Rivermead was established in the 1680s, it would have been equipped with basic water-powered stampers to prepare the pulp; their limitations have been mentioned. An improved machine, operating on a rotary principle, appeared in Holland some time between 1630 and 1665. It was called, appropriately, a Hollander (or Beater), and it produced pulp very much more rapidly than the hammer-type stampers. The complaint against John Hockley in 1733 arose because he had, allegedly, 'erected a weir which penned back and raised the water so as to overflow, drown and cover the said closes [meadows] and wash down the banks'. This was done so that he could work 'some new engine by him erected in his mill'. Thus it is possible that Hockley installed a Hollander machine in 1733, when such machines may well have been a novelty in the region.

Even with the assistance of such new machinery, paper-making was a laborious affair, particularly when white paper was being made. There was a distinction between the requirements for producing white paper, used for writing and printing, and for other papers, such as brown or blue, used for wrapping. White paper was made from white linen (first choice) or cotton rags (second choice). It needed supplies of sparkling clean water, and it required a high degree of skill. Wrapping paper was made from coloured rags, canvas, old ropes, nets and sacks. Usually it was brown, or blue, and quality was of less importance.

After the pulping all the remaining processes were entirely manual. The paper was formed on a mould, like a sieve, with a grid made up of closely spaced wires laced together and surrounded by a frame called a deckle. To make paper the vatman dipped the mould into the vat and scooped up a charge of pulp and water. After allowing the surplus water to drain off through the grid he was left with a film of wet fibres on the mould. The coucher then transferred this fibrous film from the mould onto a felt, a very delicate operation. Between them they built up a sandwich with alternate layers of felt and paper. Once the sandwich had reached the right thickness it was placed in a press to squeeze out the surplus water. The layer then separated the sheets and hung them up on lines, like washing, to dry. Hair lines were preferred, as these did not stain the paper. Local ladies may have supplied the need. A miscellany of writings, co-written and collated in 1909 by Mrs Suckling of Highwood House (now Stroud School), includes one particular memory of an aged Romsonian. This recalls how 'a woman Mary Webb with a frock smock and a tall hat used to spin hair clothes lines at the place now used by Mr G. Harris for jam potting'. (This site, now the

Waitrose supermarket, is known to have been an 18th-century sackshop run by Messrs Chapman & Pope.) Mrs Suckling also noted that 'Moll in the Wood used to live in one of the thatched cottages on the left side of the Broadway, she used to spin fine, cold and horse-hair lines'. However, spun horsehair lines were also used by fly fishermen, so the work of the industrious ladies may have related to fishing as much as to paper-making.

If pounding the pulp by water-power was slow, the subsequent manual processes were both slow and laborious. The Romsey paper-makers seem to have been spared one process, though. The rubbing of the finished paper with a smooth stone must have been minimal, since Romsey paper seems always to have had a matt, rather than a polished, surface. Even so, a one-vat mill making white paper, would probably have needed a team of eight or nine, and yet could produce only about 4,000 sheets of paper per day. There was room, therefore, for others to join this industry, and other existing Romsey mills were converted for paper-making. Mead Mill was rebuilt as a paper-mill around 1759, and Test Mill was established as a paper-mill around 1768. There is mystery attached to 'The Paper-mill in the Rope Yard', mentioned in documents written in 1772 and again in 1779; its location has not been identified. By the second half of the 18th century Romsey was in the paper-making business in a big way with at least three paper-mills, possibly four. For the remainder of the 18th century and into the first decades of the 19th century the industry thrived.

Adapting to Changes and Coping with Difficulties

Whilst the Hollander beater speeded up the production of the pulp, the remaining processes largely remained unchanged; each sheet of paper was still individually made by hand on a mould. Changes were imminent, though. In 1800 the first step was taken to mechanise paper production when the brothers Henry and Sealy Fourdrinier took out an English patent for a machine invented only shortly before in France. It took some time to develop the idea into a workable form, notably by Bryan Donkin, but machines were working in England by 1805. This machine produced paper in a continuous length, and speeded up production. By the 1830s, a time of economic crisis for many business men, the many small mills still making paper by hand were in difficulty. This may be a major reason why Mead Mill closed around this time, and probably largely accounts for the bankruptcy of William Sharp of Rivermead in 1830; and, also, why a succession of paper-makers had difficulties at Rivermead Mill following William Sharp's departure.

Dr Latham, whose early comments on the paper trade had been encouraging, felt obliged to write an 1832 addendum to the effect that paper-making in Romsey was 'now dead and the trade discontinued'. After this time, indeed, only lower grade wrapping-type paper was produced in the town. Thereafter, Romsey documents were produced on writing paper made elsewhere.

When Rivermead Mill was offered for sale in 1832, following William Sharp's bankruptcy, it was described in the sale notice as a four-vat paper-mill, a quite substantial enterprise. The notice also boasted of 'Two very powerful and never-failing streams of water, one driving three engines, the other two engines'. These engines would, almost certainly, have been beaters of the Hollander type. The mill complex also had picking shops (where the rags were sorted and cut up into handy squares), drying house, bleaching house, etc. A later sale notice of 1849 makes special mention that 'A portion of the water on the property is from springs of the purest quality and therefore valuable for the manufacture of superior paper ....'. The firm paid £5 5s 0d per annum to Lord Palmerston for the right to draw water from this spring, and the agreement included permission to lay pipes from the spring to the works. This again underlines the importance of clean water for paper-making, and may explain why paper-makers were attracted to Romsey.

During the 25 years following William Sharp's bankruptcy in 1830, a succession of three paper-makers tried to make a living at Rivermead Mill. Each lasted only four or five years, further evidence of the difficulties of the times. Around 1856 hopes must have been heightened when Captain John Harcourt Brown set up his *Brown's Patent Parchment Company*. Craven's Directory for 1857 reported '... a new establishment has lately commenced operations for the production of parchment from pulp by a patented process which will probably realise a great success'. Parchment had been made in Romsey before, by Charles Baker in 1784 at an unknown location, but this was different because it was made from bullock's hide reduced to pulp. Its novelty attracted the attentions of the revenue authorities. At that time paper was taxed, but Mr Barry, the manager at the mill, claimed that his product, being made from animal skins, was not paper and was thus not liable for the excise duty. The Courts disagreed. The hopeful promise of 1857 was not fulfilled, and some time later Rivermead Mill again fell empty. Its next occupier started a rather different enterprise making leatherboard. This was successful and continued for a hundred years. Details follow under a separate sub-heading.

Test Mill adapted to changes in paper-making technology with more success than the others. It installed modern machinery at some unspecified date, so that in 1876 the mill had one machine to make paper 60 inches wide. In 1930 Test Mill (as *Drayton's Mill*) was making 'Browns, Specialities and Toilet Paper', and the same reference states that paper-making ceased in 1939. Writing his memoirs in the 1950s, Tom Slater reported that the mill was well-known in the trade for its whitish-brown wrapping paper and that it also made brown and blue wrapping papers. The building was substantially altered in 1947. Despite the success of Mr Busby's polystyrene business (1962-1976), the final activities at Test Mill before it closed in 1995 no longer related to the paper industry.

Nevertheless, Test Mill was the last mill to make paper in Romsey, and, when production stopped, an era of paper-making that had lasted nearly three hundred years came to an end.

4   Flax & Hemp Milling

Romsey's earlier dependence on the woollen trade has been well publicised, but a later association with textiles, specifically the manufacture of flax and hemp, is less well-known. Nevertheless, Romsey did have a substantial flax-mill and it must, at the time, have made a significant contribution to the economy of the town, employing a large number of people.

The first reliable reference to this mill comes in 1822, when an inquest was held on a 14 year old girl named Fielder, who had been killed whilst working at the flax-mill belonging to Mr Lintott. The mill was very close to the Abbey corn-mill, as shown on Figure 3. The site, together with the corn-mill and most of the area now occupied by La Sagesse Convent, had been bought by William Henry Lintott in 1813. So this fixes the flax-mill's starting date somewhere between 1813 and 1822. By 1823 it was listed in Pigot's Directory as 'Wm. Lintott and Sons, Flax Spinners, Abbey Mills'.

Edward Buckell, writing in 1902, recalled that 'there were many spinning wheels formerly kept in cottages but after the factory in the Abbey was finished these disappeared'. In the early days of the flax-mill Dr Latham wrote 'a large manufactory for twine and sacks is carried on by Mr Lintott who has recently built a large mill by which much of the work is carried on by a water-wheel which gives motion to machinery within. Two or three others of the same kind are seen here but on a less scale and worked by manual labour only'. To this, as with the paper-making trade, he regretfully added a note of May 1832, stating that the work was 'now dead and the trade and materials now selling by auction'. Dr Latham's observation that the mill was up for sale is confirmed by an advertisement of 14th May 1832. Lot No 1 included the flax-mill, three storeys high and adjoining the corn-mill, whilst another lot included 'two extensive buildings .... lately used by Mr Lintott as stores and workshops for manufacturing hemp and flax with the Coal Yard'. An impression of the site, reconstructed from this advertisement, is offered in Figure 3. Mr Lintott lived in the original part of Abbey House, now enlarged eastwards into the convent of the Sisters of La Sagesse. It was a splendid house, but set in the midst of what must have been a very busy industrial area.

It seems reasonable to suppose that the mill was using power-driven machines for spinning flax and hemp yarns. Dr Latham's statement suggests that some of the yarn was used in the mill for making sacks. This idea is re-inforced by an entry in Pigot's Directory for 1830, which describes the business as 'Wm Lintott and Sons, Sack Manufacturers and Coal Merchants'.

By 1832 the mill had been forced to close. On 26th March of that year *The Hampshire Chronicle* published an interesting story, which is worth quoting in full, since it indicates the extent to which the people of Romsey looked to the mills for employment. 'On Monday a meeting took place at the Town Hall (J. George Esq. in the chair) to consider the best mode of relieving the manufacturing poor now unemployed in consequence of the trade of several of the mills and factories being suspended. Mr Footner having offered the use of the Abbey Flax-mills for a few months gratis, it was resolved that hemp should be purchased and the poor employed in its manufacture at a modest scale of wages until they can get work elsewhere.' This would seem to have been a good and practical idea, but only two months later the mill was up for sale. It must have recovered to some degree, however, because in 1838 it was said to employ 36 hands.

By the spring of 1842, maybe earlier, Samuel Thompson had taken over. He had already been operating a similar factory at East Mill in Fordingbridge for some years, and he continued to run the Romsey mill for many years to come. In 1847 his business appeared in trade directories as 'Flax-mills and Sack Manufacturers': in 1852 it was described as 'Flax and Hemp Spinners and Sack Manufacturers'; and in 1859 as 'Sacking and Canvas Manufacturers and Flax and Hemp Spinners'. Spinning was clearly important; the 1851 Census for Romsey included nine twine spinners.

Samuel Thompson was still being assessed for Land Taxes in 1864-5, but the firm does not appear in Kelly's Directory for 1867, and a useful contribution to Romsey's economy had come to an end.

5   Sawmilling

Mechanical saws, powered by water-wheels, are thought to have existed in France in the 13th century, and it is thought that the idea reached England in the 16th or 17th century. In the early days all mechanical saws would have been of the reciprocating type, driven by a crank from the shaft of the water-wheel. Circular saws came later, and the patent for these was taken out in 1762 by Walter Taylor and his son (also Walter) in Southampton. A portrait of Walter Taylor junior, holding a circular saw, is on view in Southampton's Tudor House Museum.

Romsey, seemingly, was not inspired by this technology; there are no early records of water-power being used for timber-working until the Victorian era. It may be that, although sawmilling had been introduced to Romsey on a small scale, the coming of the railway was the motivation required for making it truly viable - even if for only a limited period.

An introductory paragraph in Kelly's Directory for 1852 notes that 'here are extensive sawmills where sleepers for the adjacent railways are manufactured'. This is plausible; Romsey's first railway line, from Bishopstoke to Salisbury, opened in 1847, thus coinciding with the emergence of the town's sawmills. At Greatbridge, part of this railway line 'crosses the river and the low meadows by a timber viaduct more than 400 yards long resting on massive piles. Timber alone cost about £20,000'. This timber-work was later replaced by an earth embankment, still there today. Sawmilling probably continued to gain work from the railway, for the Andover to Southampton line was not completed until 1865.

Three sawmills driven by water-power are known to have existed in 19th-century Romsey. Probably the first of these was operated in a building on the Rivermead Mill site. A sale notice of 1832 announced that George Sharp was the tenant, and he was still there in 1849, when the mill was again offered for sale. In 1851 the sawmill was operated by Mr Thomas Westcott, and on 2nd August of that year a newspaper reported that his son had injured his hand resulting in the loss of fingers. A plan accompanying the sale notice of 1849 shows another sawmill on a separate thread of the stream; this was probably also worked by a water-wheel. It also shows a saw-pit, which was not close to any stream and could well have been worked by hand.

The oil-and-skin mill adjacent to Sadler's Mill had been converted to a sawmill around 1851, and in 1852 the operator was listed in Hunt's Directory as John Bye. It could not have lasted for long because a mortgage agreement of 1865 records that the buildings 'were some time since pulled down'. Perhaps this enterprise was over-dependent on the railway work. No trace of the mill now remains.

Another sawmill was in Middlebridge Street, a little way downstream from the Town Mill on the site now occupied by *Mitchell's Garage*. Kelly's Directory of 1855 lists the owners as William and Thomas Streeter. Its water-wheel was turned by water discharged from the Town Mill, and in 1877 Mr A.F. Streeter, the occupier at the time, was paying the owners of the Town Mill £25 per annum for the privilege of using the water. By 1892 the ownership had passed to Henry Wheeler, who now paid only £10 per annum for the water. A plan drawn by local surveyor, James Jenvey, shows that the sawmill was still there in 1905.

6.   Manufacture of Leatherboards

This is the continuing story of the Rivermead Mill. It followed a slightly different course, although still closely related to paper-making. Some time after Captain Harcourt Brown had closed his Patent Parchment Factory, Emmanuel Randall set the mill up again to manufacture 'Patent Leather', a name usually given to a highly polished leather, fashionable for dancing shoes. It seems strange that a mill previously associated with paper should switch to leather manufacture and even more surprising when later references describe it as a 'leatherboard mill'. The explanation may be found in the 1878 report of Romsey's local surveyor, James Jenvey, to whom an immense debt of gratitude is due for much information about Romsey's mills. He noted that '... the Machinery and Plant with which the premises have been fitted were initially designed and are now mainly used for the manufacture of Artificial Leather but very recently a set of costly machinery has been fitted for Paper-making in consequence of which the premises are now fully adapted for carrying on an extensive business in the manufacture of both commodities'. Thus the 'Patent Leather' was, in this connection 'Artificial Leather', a substitute leather made from paper pulp.

Mr Jenvey's report was commissioned in connection with the financial difficulties of the then owner, Mr Randall. The mill was subsequently acquired by Mr William Williams, and he became ensconced in Rivermead mill-house. According to his grand-daughter, Mrs P.A. Wellington (1905-1996), Mr Williams' interest in the mill was purely financial, and this may explain why the firm continued to trade under the name of E. Randall and Co. for many years. In 1885 Mr Williams' company was taking advantage of the facilities to manufacture varied commodities, making Brown's patent compressed leather and leatherboards, using two machines of 60-inch width (1.5 metres) and two vats. In 1897 William Williams was making 'Leather Boards, Glazed Press Papers, Jaquard and Dobie Cards' (the latter being the punched cards used to control the patterns on fancy looms). Using two machines, four vats and water-power, the mill produced 8 tons per week. Mr Williams' son, Lewis Williams, took over control of the mill from his father; in 1917 the mill was making leatherboards, glazed and shank boards, stiffeners, etc., still with two machines, four vats and water-power.

The mill continued to make leatherboards right up to its closure in 1967, although the trading name changed to *Romsey Board Mills* in the mid 1950s. Much is known of the 'Board' mill's later life as many former employees have related their stories. By 1945 it was quite a substantial enterprise employing 40 people. The process was very similar to that used for paper-making, but now the raw material was waste paper itself. After sorting, it was first chopped fine in a machine with rotating knives called a pulper. Then a modified Hollander machine, called a breaker, produced a coarse pulp which, after the addition of dyes, was refined by two more Hollander beaters. This was the supply to the board machine, which produced boards 66 inches by 44 inches and of various thicknesses. At this time there was only one machine, despite there having been two up until 1917 at least. A new second machine was installed in the 1950s, built in the mill's own workshops. This new machine incorporated an ingenious device to cut the board whilst it was still rotating, and of which the engineers were justifiably proud.

Like paper, the sheets were assembled into a stack interspersed with cloths and then pressed to remove surplus water. They were then taken off to drying rooms. Here there was shrewd use of energy. Even in these later stages of its life, much of the power needed to work the mill was supplied by water-power, making full use of the natural power available. This power was, however, augmented by a steam-engine. Adhering to the principles of energy conservation, the exhaust steam from the engine was used to heat the drying rooms. The steam pipes also passed through greenhouses where tomatoes were grown.

Final finishing processes involved trimming to size, 'callendering' between heated rollers to bring out a smooth surface and finally packing for despatch. In the 1920s, though, the firm not only made the board but used some to make shoe stiffeners. One Romsey lady recalls how, as a young girl, she worked a machine to cut the shapes from the board. Later, the firm concentrated on board manufacture alone. After 1939 some of the production went to a small company close by called *The Varnished Fibreboard Company*, run by two partners, Steiner and Mantner. They employed about eight people, and they applied a textured finish to the boards, which were then sent to other firms to be made into suitcases and similar commodities.

7   Tanning

Romsey, like many towns, had tanneries from at least the 13th to the 20th century. As a general rule they were located downstream, so that the noxious effluents could be discharged without too much offence to the townspeople. In Romsey they were mostly located in Middlebridge Street, which met this requirement. But there was one interesting exception; there appears to have been a tannery right in the centre of the town, on the site later occupied by the *Horsefair Brewery*. It survived into the early part of the 19th century when it was in the hands of a widow, Mrs Grist, the last of a family that had worked the tannery for around 70 years.

Although water was essential to the various processes of converting animal skins into leather, many of the early tanneries undoubtedly operated without the assistance of water-power. Eventually, the primary requirement for water-power in the tanneries was to drive the bark-mills. The first bark-mills worked by crushing the bark under a heavy stone wheel with a serrated rim that rolled around a circular track. The preferred bark was from oak trees, and was locally available. These mills ground bark into a coarse powder, which was then steeped in water for several weeks to produce a solution of tannin, the essential ingredient for curing the hides. An interesting advertisement in 1832 offered bark from oak trees in the New Forest for sale 'at the pole'. Lot 1, for example, included the bark from 45 Navy Oak Trees and 500 Casual Oak Trees at Lyndhurst Hill and Buckhill in Lyndhurst and Boldrewood Walks.

There are records of two Romsey water-driven bark-mills. A 1784 report about the rebuilding of Middlebridge mentions a bark-mill by the south-east corner of the old bridge. It had a house over it and a kiln for drying the bark. Unfortunately, it was in the way of progress and was demolished in the 1770s, so that the approach to the new bridge could be widened.

The second of these bark-mills was in Middlebridge Street, adjacent to, and just to the north of, *The Three Tuns* public house. It is thought to be of later date than the other mill. It had an iron water-wheel powered by the Holbrook Stream. The water had been discharged from the Town Mill, and had already passed through the water-wheel at the sawmill further upstream. Finally, it drove the wheel at the tannery. The water still cost money. Mr Charles Fluder-Smith, who had the tannery in 1877, paid £7 per annum to the owners of Town Mill as owners of the stream bed. In 1892, Fluder-Smith's successor, James Baker, was still paying £7. This was good business for the Town Mill, whose owner also collected from the sawmill for the same water.

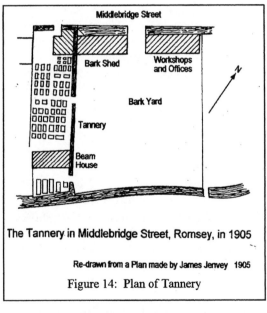

The Tannery in Middlebridge Street, Romsey, in 1905

Re-drawn from a Plan made by James Jenvey 1905

Figure 14: Plan of Tannery

More is known of the tannery near the Three Tuns, courtesy of an inventory prepared by James Jenvey, the local surveyor, in 1905. The tannery at that time had 63 tanning pits, a bark yard and bark rick; the water-wheel drove not only the bark-mill but also the pumps that fed the tanning pits. By that time it is most likely that the bark-mill would have been an iron machine working on the same principle as the pepper-mill now so popular on dining tables.

The Middlebridge Street tannery closed in 1926. The water-wheel no longer performed any useful purpose, but it did remain in place for some time afterwards. Many local residents remember it before its removal in the early

1950s. In 1997 the site was completely cleared for redevelopment, and the last remaining vestige of a tannery, an iron slideway for the water-wheel hatch, finally disappeared.

8   Other Uses for Water-Power

Using Water to Move Water

Water-wheels, using the power of falling water, could themselves raise water for use in homes, factories or simply to work an ornamental fountain. Broadlands had such a water-wheel in the early years of the 18th century, and it caught the imagination of Celia Fiennes. She wrote 'there is a water house that by a Wheele casts up the water out of the River just by and fills the pipes to serve all the house and to fill the bason designed in the middle of the Garden with a Spout in the middle'. There was also a water-wheel at Timsbury, to the north of Romsey, and this pumped water up to Timsbury Manor.

Within the town, a water pump at Fox Mill was amongst equipment removed from the mill in the early 1970s. This pump may have been used in connection with the creamery, established there in the 1890s as *The Farmer's Direct Milk Co.* The machinery included two cream separators, a milk pump, water pumps, a large refrigerator and a cream refrigerator. The water-wheel was retained, but anxiety about the water supply clearly continued, since the wheel was supplemented by a 1.5 horse-power engine. In 1898 Mitchells started their motor engineering business at Fox Mill. In the First World War they produced shell cases at the rate of between 1,000 and 1,800 per week.

Crushing Bones and Chalk

According to the 1849 plan of the Rivermead site *(see Figure 5 on page 48)* a secondary building, also closely adjacent to a stream, was worked as a bone-crushing mill, presumably producing fertilisers. Perhaps more interestingly, the plan also shows an 'Engine House' but the description makes no mention of a steam-engine. Possibly the building housed a boiler from the earlier days when the site was home to a paper-mill. By any account this was a busy industrial site in 1849, with a wide range of uses.

There was another interesting application at Town Mill, and this also made additional demands on the power supply. Close by the corn-mill there was a whiting-mill, which had a machine for grinding chalk. It was driven from the main shaft of the corn-mill. Since the whiting mill was in a separate

94

building there must have been some kind of rotating drive-shaft crossing the yard. There is no record of how this was accomplished, but simultaneous use of the whiting-mill and the corn-mill certainly did cause problems. A report written in 1878 notes that: 'There is no existing means of rapid communication between the Whiting Mill and the Town Mill and it frequently happens that the machinery of the former is suddenly put in motion or as suddenly stopped, by which the speed of the water-wheel, which is at the same time driving the mill-stones, is instantly checked or accelerated. This variation in the speed of the water-wheel consequently affects the working of the stones so much that the quality of the flour or meal is deteriorated ....'. It may have been more trouble than it was worth. When Town Mill was offered for sale in 1881, the property included a 'spacious yard in part of which are several pits lately used in the manufacture of whiting'. Presumably, the whiting-mill had closed a short time previously.

Turbines, Dynamos & Electricity

Mains drainage in Romsey dates from the early 1930s. Very close to Sadler's Mill there is a long, low building, which housed two pumps for transferring sewage to the treatment plant at Greenhill. Power for the pumps was provided by two turbines. The building is still there, but its duties have been taken over by electrically-driven pumps housed in a new building nearby.

Electricity came late to Romsey; it was gradually introduced from the late 1920s onwards. It became convenient to harness the water-power available at several of the mill sites to drive private electric generators. One such plant was installed in Sadler's Mill to provide electricity for Broadlands and for some of the farms on the estate. It was driven by a turbine and continued to work until the late 1960s. In 1927 Burnt Mill was occupied by Victor Moyer Tate, trading as *Burnt Mill Electric Dynamos*; unfortunately nothing more is known of this enterprise. When corn-grinding ended at Greatbridge Mill one of the water-wheels was adapted to drive a dynamo, and this extended the useful life of that mill for many more years.

After the Abbey Mill had burned down in 1925 a new building was erected on the original foundations, in which the wheelhouse had been located. The new building was completed around 1928 as part of the Convent of the Sisters of La Sagesse. When the building was erected, the opportunity was taken to utilise the water-power by installing two new turbines within the suitably modified wheelhouse. These turbines provided electricity for the whole site for many years. Mr Ormsby recalls that Town Mill was also lit by a dynamo driven from the main shaft. When water was short and the hoist was being operated to raise sacks of grain to the upper floors, the additional load would slow the whole system down; and the lights would go dim.

Variety of Uses

The sawmill in Middlebridge Street was taken over by Mitchells Motors in 1919, and they continued to utilise the power of the water-wheel right up until 1958. The wheel drove engineering machinery, and at one time it was also connected to a generator. Many residents remember taking radio batteries to be recharged until the 1950s.

Finale

Mills were full of combustible material, and fire was an inherent danger. Even though some burnt down more than once, they were always rebuilt for the sake of the power supplied through the force of the river and its braids. Romsey's waterways provided the motive power for the town mills for at least 900 years. It was only some thirty years ago that the water was finally allowed to flow freely without being called upon to drive the mill-stones, fulling stocks, paper pulp-beaters or electric generators. Yet the power taken from the river neither radically hindered its progress nor impaired its quality in any way. The river never complained nor asked for payment. But the chapter is now closed and the power is simply left to run into the sea.

Abbey Mill, Romsey. Destroyed by Fire, 1925.

Figure 15
Abbey Mill at the west end of Abbey Water
by Sybil Panton

96

NON-MILLING ACTIVITIES
ON ROMSEY'S WATERWAYS

Water-mills were inevitable at Romsey, given the opportunities offered by the River Test and its many braids. Long before and after the development of water-mills, however, the people of Romsey had other uses for the readily available but jealously guarded water.

Many and varied craftsmen, operating in small workshops, took advantage of the waterways for some part of their process. Certain non-milling activities were particularly dependent on heavy use of water. These were largely urban-based, in Romsey taking advantage of the twin strands of the Fishlake. Those who ran such activities, though, were generally answerable to the mill-owners, who strictly controlled use of their mill-streams.

Iron-smelting

Long before mills dictated such stringent controls, Romsey's iron-smelting industry evolved in the mid-Saxon period. It was centred to the west of the present Newton Lane carpark, and extended over some five acres. It probably endured from the 7th to the early 10th century, indicating an early importance for the town. The location combined a toe-hold on the southern part of the dry land on which Romsey was founded with proximity to an early line of the Shitlake. Water would have been essential to the life and work of this community, which marks the beginning of a continuity of settlement that cannot be proven in Romsey for any earlier times.

The location and terrain of Romsey were extremely convenient for early iron-smelting. The iron ore, mostly box-ore, could be brought across the river. Firewood was in plentiful supply from the woodland areas that later became known as the New Forest, Buckholt Forest and West Bere Forest, all then fringing the town. A convenient market for the iron produced on this site might well have been Hamwic, Southampton's Saxon settlement.

Fishponds, Fisheries and Water Gardens

The arrival of the nuns, by the early 10th century, placed emphasis on fish as a key part of the convent diet. Herrings were imported through Southampton, and cartloads destined for Romsey are recorded in the medieval brokage books that detail goods passing through the Southampton Bargate. At Romsey the nuns also had their supply of fresh fish kept in their fishponds. These constituted a very major farming undertaking with a crucial dependence on the nearby waterways. The site of these fishponds has been located to the west of the Abbey church, where the present vicarage now stands. Water was provided by a special cut that flowed northwards from the west end of Abbey Water. It has already been suggested that there may be a link between these fishponds and the name 'Fishlake' or 'Fishlet' for the stream that supplied them.

The tradition of fisheries has continued. From Tudor times onwards there are references to fisheries at mill sites. By the 18th century there was a major fishpond between Church Street and the east end of Romsey Abbey, though it may have been a private rather than a commercial enterprise. This fishpond took its water supply via a streamlet, controlled by a hatch, off the Fishlake by No 6 Church Street. It may be that this watercourse had its origins in the water supply to the Abbey's domestic range.

Today, there are fish farms in the locality, particularly on the north side of Romsey. Commercial water gardens with exotic 'ornamental' fish, as well as other watery features, such as fountains, ponds and water plants, also make use of the Romsey streams.

Riverside Plants & Basket-Making

Riverside plants and trees were once a vital part of life, and Romsey's waterways offered long stretches of low-lying land on which these plants might flourish. As elsewhere, reeds were gathered for thatching, and rushes harvested for strewing on floors, for rush-lights in poor dwellings and for a variety of weaving and plaiting work that ranged from baskets to matting and chair seats. Osier beds of pliant willow produced the material for stronger baskets. Romsey's 1845 Tithe Award map records informative field names, such as 'Sedge Bed', 'Ozier Bed' or 'Great Spaniards' (a type of willow). These reflect the importance of otherwise humble and unsung trades.

Basket-making, one of the main occupations linked with river plants, also depended on water for soaking materials to be worked. Eel-traps were of basket-ware until superseded by metal, and there were countless other needs for basket containers. Before the 20th century it was generally a low status trade. Then, in the 1920s and 1930s, a long-established Romsey basket-making family, the Iremongers, ran a superior business in The Hundred. They sold their products, including basket perambulators, to Harrod's. Due to the labour-intensive nature of the work, this company did not survive, but individual basket-makers have continued to work in and around the town.

Industries Alongside the Urban Millstreams

The Holbrook on its way to Town Mill, and later the Fishlake as it approached Abbey Mill, gradually became the focus for various water-dependent activities. Church Street, the northerly arm extending from Romsey's Market Place, occupied a unique position between the two. Its medieval history, however, suggests that it began mainly as a high status area with large holdings held by clerics and gentry, as might be expected of its proximity to the Abbey precinct. Industry on an extensive scale had to wait.

Dyeing

Medieval dyeing, the first noteworthy industry to take advantage of the Holbrook Stream, was suitably to the east of Church Street. On the north-west edge of the Holbrook in Portersbridge Street there was an early 14th-century dye-shop, where the property known as *The Coachhouse* now stands. The dye-shop belonged to Alexander Dyer, sometimes described more exotically in Latin form as Alexander Tinctor. A century later, and the same spot was occupied by another dyer called John Busshe. Other unknown dyers may well have occupied this convenient location with its good supply of essential water. The finishing of woollen cloth was the major industry that brought prosperity to medieval Romsey. Whilst the most notable aspect of this industry was the fulling, carried out in mills as already described, dyeing also played an important part. It lasted as a Romsey occupation until the beginning of the 18th century.

After the dissolution of the Abbey in 1539 the tenor of Church Street itself changed. The large properties were fragmented, and the street became the hub of a variety of industries. All made good use of the twin branches of the Fishlake/Holbrook that bounded their properties. Dyers spread into this area and archaeologists have found evidence of dyeing vats, probably 17th-century in date, on both sides of the street - just behind the Abbey Walk shops on the east and slightly further north on the west side. In addition to those locations identified by the archaeologists, documents suggest that there were other 17th-century clothworkers on the east side of Church Street.

Bronze-Working and Shoemaking

Although not so heavily dependent on water as the dyers, the braziers and shoemakers of Church Street would have counted themselves fortunate to be in such an enviable position. Interestingly, two buildings in which they operated still survive. One is King John's House, a 13th-century stone building just off the east side of Church Street. It had belonged to the Abbey at the time of the dissolution, but later became home to an unknown brazier. Archaeologists have found evidence of his workshop, again probably 17th-century in date. The shoemaker, on the other hand, has been discovered from documentary evidence. He was John Cox, mayor of Romsey in 1660, and he lived in the building now occupied by The Oasis Christian Centre.

Coopering

To the north of present Abbey Walk yet another craftsman added to the diversity of 17th-century industry in this area. He was a cooper by the name of Thomas Voakes, and would have been very dependent on the water supply for the soaking of wood prior to shaping. The inventory of Mr Voakes' stock-in-trade, taken after his death in 1695, suggests a sizeable concern. He must have died whilst still a thriving businessman. Besides his domestic possessions, his inventory included working tools and a large amount of work in progress. These ranged from finished items, such as 15 buckets and 3 humberkins to material ready for making an assortment of goods. 700 tub bottoms were worth £7 and 42 dozen 'small bottoms' were appraised at £1 15s 0d. Specialised timber included some designated for firkins and hogsheads, whilst 4,400 pieces worth £5 17s 0d were waiting to be made into pails, seemingly Mr Voakes' most popular product.

Breweries

Brewing took place throughout Romsey, taking sparkling fresh water from wells and depending on the streams to carry away the effluents. In Church Street a 17th-century brewer by the name of Thomas Cuffley either preceded or followed the brazier in King John's House. Unlike the brazier he is only known about through documents, leaving no physical evidence of his presence in the house. Most early innkeepers, though, brewed their own beer on the premises. The Falcon, on the site of The Abbey Hotel in Church Street, was one such inn. Then, as transport improved, common brewers began to operate on a comparatively large scale at the end of the 18th century. Numerous specialised breweries emerged, and they began to acquire public houses 'tied' to their products. The Falcon Inn was one of those that ceased to brew independently, being taken over initially by *Trodd & Hall*, one of Romsey's first common brewers. By the middle of the 19th century the best known were the *Jesser & Cressey Brewery* (otherwise *The Hundred Brewery* from its location), the *George Brewery* in Bell Street, and *Thomas Strong's Brewery* off The Horsefair at the end of Church Street. *The Hundred Brewery* had the Tadburn Stream to the south, whilst the other two were located on the Fishlake/Holbrook.

Then, in the 1880s, David Faber came to Romsey, and amalgamated these and other local breweries to form the great company called *Strong & Co. Ltd.* David Faber's new company helped to restore the town's economy, flagging since the railway had destroyed the coaching trade and related businesses. The main centre of this brewery, on a vast site behind the north-east end of modern Church Street, gave it the alternative title of *The Horsefair Brewery*. At the brewery's north end the Fishlake Stream split into its two branches, the easterly Holbrook in particular dissecting the property, whilst the other branch more or less edged the western boundary of the site. Many were the disagreements between the Romsey Corporation and the brewery about the state of the water as it emerged from the 'heart of the Strong country'. Its objectionable effluents polluted both the water itself and the atmosphere in general; but the town was very dependent on the success of the business and the complaints had little effect. *Strong & Co. Ltd* gave employment to many Romsonians for some ninety years or so, but, after being taken over by Whitbreads, the brewery was demoted to a bottling plant and finally closed.

Steam Sawmills
Sawmills were established in the Portersbridge Street/Station Road area during the 19th and early 20th century. Although often referred to as timber-yards, implying simply a storage of timber, these enterprises were rather more than that. Any power used, however, was produced by steam-engine rather than water-power, since the owners of Town Mill would not have allowed any water-wheels up-stream of their activities. A supply of water would have been needed for a steam-engine, and the business as a whole would have been dependent on a certain use of water. It was convenient for timber-yards to be adjacent to a stream - the Holbrook in this instance.

The O.S. map of 1867 shows two timber-yards in the Portersbridge Street area, one on the north side and a larger one on the south side behind the garden of King John's House. Robert Lillington Fluder's sawmill in Portersbridge Street is listed in White's Directory of 1859. Mrs Suckling of Highwood House noted that 'Fluder's timber-yard reached to nearly opposite Stead Tylee and Mortimer's Offices' (No 2 Portersbridge Street). As these offices were on the north side, Fluder's saw-works must have been on the site to the south.

Mr Fluder was succeeded by William James Fox, who continued to run the site as a timber-yard/sawmill. There was probably an agreement with the owner of Town Mill to take, or pump, a limited amount of water from the stream at approved times. The Berthon Boatyard, which succeeded William James Fox, certainly had a very comprehensive and restrictive agreement with the Town Mill.

After leaving Portersbridge Street, William James Fox had a steam sawmill in Station Road in 1878. By 1900 he had been succeeded by Charles William Fox. The Station Road site was probably far less convenient, but Mr Fox had financial difficulties and would have had to make the best of things. Steam-engines would certainly have been obligatory on his new site which was some way from any water; but there is no evidence about the water supply for this business.

The Berthon Boatyard

The Berthon Boatyard, which replaced the timber-yard to the south of Portersbridge Street, offered employment to a considerable number of Romsonians in the late Victorian and Edwardian periods. It was an unexpected enterprise for an inland market town such as Romsey, set up even more unexpectedly by the Vicar of Romsey, Rev. Edward Lyon Berthon. He had entered the Church only after a career as a doctor and with a life-long interest in engineering. Even after taking holy orders he retained his love of invention, and continued with the development of his own engineering ideas. The vicarage garden was the first site of his successful work on folding boats and other collapsible structures, such as bandstands. He tested the boats on the stretch of Test Mill Stream that flowed along the bottom of his garden. Little is heard of any objection to the vicar's attention being so diverted. Perhaps too many inhabitants were grateful for the work he created.

Eventually, indeed, the work became too much for the garden, or its use was challenged. In 1877 he acquired the Portersbridge Street premises described above. This new site eventually expanded to reach over a 72 feet length of the Holbrook Stream. Water from the Holbrook was crucial to his work, especially in topping up the timber-pond that was a big feature of the yard.

In 1890 the company was paying an annual wayleave of £1 for the right to erect a building 'over the stream near Portersbridge Street and to use water for a timber-yard'. This new building must be made only of timber and iron 'so that the floors of the said buildings be laid on or above the existing walls of the stream and that they be so constructed and at such a height as not to impede the flow of the said stream in flood time'. The Boatyard also acquired the right to another bridge over the stream, and for this paid an annual quit rent of 2s 6d. Other terms of agreement between the boatyard and the owners of the Town Mill illustrate well the very keen control exerted by the mill-owners over other users of their waterways. Besides the right to take out water for the timber-pond, the company also gained the right to use a temporary pump about six times a year 'to pump water into the boiler of the engines at work on the said Works'. Surface water only might be drained and discharged into the stream from the Company cottages newly erected in Portersbridge Street and described as odd numbers 1-13. In return for these extra rights the Company was to pay £2 3s 6d, and had to promise not to interfere with the existing walls on either side of the stream, or the flow of the water to the mill. The stream should never be polluted or obstructed. The mill-owners' rights and interests in the stream must be paramount.

Surviving Features

Throughout the known story of Romsey the waterways have given impetus to many industrial activities. Not all these activities have made such heavy use of the waterways as those indicated above, but all had a vital need for some use of water in their working lives as well as for domestic purposes. Two surviving features in Romsey serve as reminders of the many and varied uses of its waterways, and the ways in which the water was extracted from them. In the lower part of Middlebridge Street, on the south side, some surviving railings have a couple of strange variations introduced. These variations created space that allowed hoses to be lowered for steam-engine vehicles to take up water before leaving town via Middlebridge.

Plate 8
19th-century privies over the Holbrook
at the rear of King John's House

Then, at the rear of King John's House, where the Holbrook now trickles past the newly created historic gardens, there is a dipping point, a recess in the stream bank that allowed the inhabitants of Church Court to raise bucketfuls of water - just upstream from their privies.

HAMPSHIRE.

PARTICULARS & CONDITIONS OF SALE

OF A VALUABLE

FREEHOLD ESTATE

(WITH POSSESSION),

WELL SITUATED

NEAR THE TOWN AND RAILWAY STATION AT ROMSEY,

Eight Miles from Southampton, 10 from Winchester, and 15 from Salisbury,

COMPRISING A CAPITAL

WATER CORN MILL,

IN THOROUGH WORKING ORDER, DOING AN OLD-ESTABLISHED BUSINESS,

AND HAVING A

COMFORTABLE RESIDENCE,

With all SUITABLE OUT-BUILDINGS, and FOUR LABOURERS' COTTAGES;

ALSO

24a. 2r. 9p.

OF FERTILE ARABLE, PASTURE, AND MEADOW LAND.

For Sale by Auction

AT THE MART, TOKENHOUSE YARD, BANK OF ENGLAND,

On WEDNESDAY, the 12th day of MAY, 1880

(AT TWO O'CLOCK PRECISELY),

BY MESSRS.

EDWIN FOX AND BOUSFIELD

Of whom Particulars and Conditions of Sale may be had at their Office in Gresham Street; at the Mart; at the White Horse, Romsey; at the Inns at Winchester, Salisbury, and Southampton; of C. M. REEVES, Esq., Surveyor, 102, Guilford Street, W.C.; and of Messrs.

G. B. FOOTNER & SON,
Solicitors,
Romsey.

EDWIN FOX.
E. H. BOUSFIELD. } "EDWIN FOX AND BOUSFIELD."
EDWIN FOX, JUN. } 90, GRESHAM STREET, BANK, E.C.

Figure 16
Sale Notice for Greatbridge Mill, 1880

CONCLUSION

The waterways of Romsey may no longer be so vital to the working lives of the local inhabitants, but they form a key feature of the town's character. The Fishlake/Holbrook streams, in particular, have helped to create the still surviving lay-out of the town, and provide attractive breaks in the townscape.

Yet, whilst inhabitants and visitors to Romsey find pleasure in the waterways, they may lack the keen awareness of the River Test's great contribution to the town that was felt by Romsonians of past centuries. This awareness certainly persisted in the 19th century, when the river's importance crept into often unrelated contexts.

Perhaps this may be illustrated by some rather excruciating lines, written - and acknowledged as doggerel - on the occasion of Romsey's weekly market changing from a Saturday to a Thursday on 27th April 1826. The eight verses and chorus sound suspiciously as if they were sung to the tune of *The Vicar cf Bray,* probably with great gusto and enthusiasm at the expense of musicality, but still with a heartfelt nod of appreciation to the source of much prosperity, the River Test.

The full version of this *tour-de-force,* on a printed handbill, is on display in King John's House, Romsey. The sixth verse concludes:

> 'In eating lots of Romsey Eels,
> Or Romsey's far-fam'd Trout, Sir'

The final verse and chorus are as follows:

> 'Let's give three cheers for PALMERSTON,
> The Lord of Romsey Manor;
> May still success our efforts crown,
> Beneath his Lordship's banner!
> O may each future Thursday teem,
> With Wealth and Plenty's store, Sir;
> And, like our Test's surrounding stream,
> On Romsey, treasures pour, Sir;

> > *Chorus*
> > The passing scene now bright appears,
> > The present time seems best, Sir;
> > Yet may we thro' revolving years,
> > Be oft brought to the Test, Sir.'

Acknowledgements

The writers of this book would like to acknowledge help given by fellow members of the Lower Test Valley Archaeological Study Group [LTVAS], particularly by Mr C. Burnett for his work on photographic enhancement. The support of the Hampshire Mills Group has also been crucial to this work. The resources of the Hampshire Record Office, and the kindness of their staff, have been as invaluable as ever in the research for this book, whilst the work of the Test Valley Archaeological Trust forms the background of much of the information about early Romsey.

The personal contributions of Mr B. Aldrich, Mr C. Busby, Mr M. Edgeworth, Mr L. Fairlie, Mr T. Fryer, Mr F.J. Green, Mr D. Knapman, Mr M. Lunn, Mr J. Ormsby and many others are acknowledged with much appreciation.

We are grateful to Mr I. Bowerman for the photograph of the salmon leaping by Sadler's Mill, and also to the unknown photographers of the 1911 photographs and of Middlebridge c1890. All other photographs and diagrams by G.J. Hawksley.

References and Sources

Detailed references have not been included in this book, but are available from LTVAS. However, due acknowledgement should be given to the key document in the 1807 milling dispute. This was discovered in the early 1990s and is now at the Hampshire Record Office [Ref: HRO 4M92N/240/6]. It inspired this book.

Principal Sources:
LTVAS Resources
Test Valley Archaeological Trust
Hampshire Record Office
Hampshire Mills Group
Public Record Office

Maps
1845 Tithe Award Map for Romsey & 1867 OS Maps of Romsey

Select Bibliography

Buckell, E.	The Old Watercourses and Mills of Romsey.	Hampshire Field Club Papers Vol IV (1898-1903)
Himsworth, S. (Editor)	Winchester College Muniments, Volume II	Phillimore, 1984
Latham, Dr J.	Unpublished History of Romsey	BL Mss 26774-26780
Liveing, Rev. H.	The Records of Romsey Abbey	Warren and Son, Winchester (1906)
Slater, Mr T.	Unpublished Diary, written in 1950s	LTVAS Collection
Suckling, Mrs H.	Old Romsey, Vol. I (Miscellany of Writings)	Privately bound, 1909 (LTVAS Collection)

INDEX of Romsey Waterways and related subjects/people

paper
  sugar, 53
  white, 53, 83, 84, 85
  wrapping, 53, 82, 83, 87
paper-making, 33, 47, 51, 52, 53, 82, 83, 84, 85, 86, 87, 90, 91
paper-workers, 54
Partiger, Samuel (mill-owner), 45
Pavement Commission, 14, 22
Peak stone, 71
peat bog, 10
Plyer, Matthew (paper-maker), 52
pollutants, 15
pollution, 29, 31, 33
privies, 11, 33, 103
pulper, 91

—Q—

quern, rotary, 69

—R—

racks, 80
radio batteries, 96
rags, 53, 54, 83, 84, 86
Randall, Emmanuel (miller), 90
reeds, 98
Repeal of the Corn Laws, 75
River Test Salmon Preservation Society, 31
Rivermead, 8, 16, 47, 48, 52, 53, 56, 60, 84, 85, 91, 94
Rivermead Mill, 52, 53, 65, 68, 82, 85, 86, 89, 90
Romsey Board Mills, 91
rushes, 98
rush-lights, 98
Rysbrygger, John (miller), 38

—S—

saddle-stone, 69
Sadler, Richard, 45

Sadler's Mill, 5, 8, 9, 27, 44, 45, 46, 47, 51, 56, 57, 66, 73, 76, 78, 80, 82, 90, 95
salmon, 20, 25, 28, 29, 30, 31
Salmon Fisheries Act, 1861, 31
Salmon Leap, 5, 56
salmon pass, 27
sewage, 95
shalloon, 50, 81
Sharp, George (miller), 89
Sharp, James (mill-owner), 50, 81
Sharp, Stephen (paper-maker), 47
Sharp, William (paper-maker), 47, 52, 53, 85, 86
Shitlake, 11, 97
shoe stiffeners, 92
shoemakers, 99
Shutlands Stream, 13
silt, 14
silting, 10, 11
Skeats, 50
Skeats, Henry (paper-maker), 52
Skeats, James (paper-maker), 50, 52
Skidmore, 72
Skidmore mill, 35
Slater, Tom, 87
sluice, 9, 14, 27, 28
smolt suppers, 28
smut machine, 74, 75
snipe, 27
Soffe, William (miller), 66
Soffe's Mill, 55
Soke, 71, 72
Special Commissioners for English Fisheries, 32
Spratt's Mill, 50
Spursholt, 44, 45, 46
steam-engine, 91, 94, 101, 102, 103
Steiner and Mantner, 92
stew ponds, 28, 30
still waters, 11, 15, 39
Straight Stream, 16, 47, 48, 83
Streeter, A.F. (sawmiller), 90

111